THE ABANDONED WOMAN

A great deal has been written about Lucy Walter, mistress of Charles II and mother of his eldest son. Most of it is conjecture, much of it untrue. Here, recreated by Frank Arthur, is the story as she herself might have told it, more than three hundred years ago. It shows her first as a young lass of fifteen, meeting her 'black boy', the Prince of Wales, and falling in love with him for life; then we see her on a journey to Paris, disguised as a boy and with the Crown Jewels tied around her waist. Welcomed by Charles, she became his mistress; but his determination to recover his crown at all costs came between them, and gradually the romantic love affair merged into the loneliness of the abandoned mistress, taunted by her enemies on every side.

The story is, perhaps, a tragic one, though there is joy and humour here as well. The gay young Prince, witty and cynical, is a really credible portrait of the boy who grew to be Charles II of history; and Lucy emerges from it all as a dynamic, passionate woman, whose beauty, even at the end, could evoke a tribute from the humble clerk who penned her story as she spoke.

BOOKS BY

FRANK ARTHUR

NOVELS

Who Killed Netta Maul?
(reprinted by Penguin as *The Suva Harbour Mystery*)

Another Mystery in Suva

Murder in the Tropic Night

The Throbbing Dark

The Abandoned Woman

ONE-ACT PLAYS

Time's a Thief

She Would Not Dance

Twenty Minutes with Mrs Oakentubb

My Love's Different

Special Lunch

Salmonella Smith

No Cracked Cups for Me

THE ABANDONED WOMAN

The Story of Lucy Walter
(1630-1658)

Frank Arthur

HEINEMANN : LONDON

William Heinemann Ltd
LONDON MELBOURNE TORONTO
CAPE TOWN AUCKLAND

First published 1964

Printed in Great Britain by
The Northumberland Press Limited
Gateshead

To

MY WIFE

Contents

'I have brought the Black Box at last, madam.'
(WILLIAM CONGREVE, *The Way of the World*)

' 'Tis a frailty they say is given to the sex;
therefore you will pardon her, I hope.'
(MARY OF ORANGE, PRINCESS ROYAL, TO HER
BROTHER, CHARLES II, ON BEHALF OF LUCY
WALTER—PERHAPS.)

Introduction

A GREAT DEAL has been written about Lucy Walter, the abandoned woman—most of it conjecture, much of it lies. The facts
of her life are either largely unknown or in dispute. She has
been rightly described by David Ogg as 'an obscure woman'.
Almost all we can be sure of is that she was born about 1630,
that her forebears were Welsh gentry with noble connections
and a trickle of royal blood on her mother's side, that she was
for a time the mistress of Charles II in exile, that she was the
mother of the Duke of Monmouth and of a daughter who was
the recipient of royal bounty all her life, and that she died in
Paris towards the end of 1658, about the same time as Oliver
Cromwell died in Whitehall.

We know, too, that her father, William Walter, owned Roch
Castle in Pembrokeshire; that he brought his wife Elizabeth and
their children to London in 1638, deserted them in 1641, and
spent the whole period of the Civil War in legal conflict with
his wife. Each side accused the other of sexual unfaithfulness and
financial trickery. Mrs Walter was a Royalist, and obtained a
sequestration order on her husband's estates in 1641; but in 1647,
when the King had been defeated and William was serving the
Parliament in Wales, the House of Lords removed the order and
directed that the children should be sent back to their father for
their keeping and education.

We do not know if Lucy (presumably well on in her teens)

returned to Wales; but she must have been with the Prince of
Wales on the Continent by the middle of 1648, for he acknowledged the son she bore at Rotterdam on 9 April 1649. By that
date the Prince of Wales was titular Charles II; and Lucy Walter
(who had assumed, for reasons which are unknown, the name
of Barlow) was his accepted mistress for some time. She is reported
as claiming that he spent a night with her in 1656, by which year
he certainly had other mistresses and children; he was sending
her money and promises as late as December 1657, and one of
his household arranged for her burial in 1658.

That would have been the end of her in history had not her
son been put forward as Protestant heir to the throne against the
King's Catholic brother, the Duke of York (James II). During
the turbulent years of the Popish Plot and the Exclusion Bill
struggle it was rumoured that Lucy, on her death-bed in Paris,
had confided the story of her life and her marriage certificate to
the Anglican pastor, Dean Cosin, later Bishop of Durham; and
that the bishop had placed these documents in a Black Box, and
given it to his heirs with strict instructions to keep it unopened
until Charles II died. A wide-ranging official enquiry in 1680
failed to find any trace either of the Black Box or of the marriage.
This book is Lucy's life story as it might have been preserved in
the Black Box if the Black Box had existed.

It has frequently been alleged, both during her lifetime and
since, that Lucy was not faithful to the King. Her reputation
in history (and in historical fiction) is that of 'an ill woman'
and a common whore. But it is not certain that this is the truth.
Men were liars even in the days of Titus Oates. And many of
her contemporaries who branded her as infamous had very strong
political reasons for wishing to destroy her. The problems presented by her career are four: was she married to Charles II?
was he the father of her son? was he the father of her daughter?
was she a common prostitute? Many writers have decided against
her on all four counts, and most have decided against her on all
but the second. But there is room for doubt in her favour on all
four.

The story in this book, told from Lucy's point of view, is based on contemporary records of her actions in so far as these have survived, and on my assessment of the characters of the men and women who influenced her career. Where no records exist and I have had to invent episodes, I have been careful (except in one instance) to keep within the bounds of historical possibility.

In the Appendix I have reproduced or summarised almost all the contemporary references to Lucy, and the reader may, if so moved, decide for himself where the truth lay and where the malice. Most historical writers and novelists who mention Lucy have taken their facts almost entirely from the *Memoirs* of James II or from Clarendon. I have neither reproduced these hostile (and contradictory) statements in my Appendix nor attempted to refute them there in detail; they are long, they are well-known, and my reasons for disbelieving most of what they say will be given in the non-fiction study of Lucy Walter which I have in preparation. It is not to be expected that Lucy's own story would confirm all that her enemies said about her. She has been the target for malignant slander for three centuries. It is time she should be allowed to speak for herself. So the story in this book purports to be her voice pleading her case from the unrecorded grave where her once-lovely body has mouldered these three hundred years.

It is evident from the first-hand records of her actions that Lucy was passionate and voluble, though these adjectives are nowhere used by contemporaries who describe her; and she may well have related the story of her life in the breathless style of these memoirs. It does not follow, of course, that, even if these pages were authentic, they would be truthful. Her protestations of eternal fidelity to the man who had used her so ill, and her habit of piously rounding-off each episode, may well have been intended to impress Dean Cosin. The piety may indeed have been inserted by the Dean or his amanuensis. But whether true or not, there is little in these memoirs which can be proved untrue by such impartial evidence as has survived.

Finally, remember this: Lucy Walter was beautiful, she was bold, she was Welsh; a King loved her; she was unfortunate; and she died young. If she was frail, it was because a man would have her so. 'Therefore you will pardon her, I hope.'

Bromley, Kent   Frank Arthur
October 1957-February 1964

I Wales: The Beginning (July 1645)

WHEN HIS SACRED MAJESTY, King Charles the First, came to Golden Grove (said Mistress Barlow) his cause was in parlous state, and he was in no mood for gaiety. For that matter, he was always grave and quiet, I remember, even in the days past when he maintained his authority and state as King in London, and I, a little girl combed and curled and scented, was carried with my Sidney or my Howard cousins to St James's to play with the royal children. It was the Queen who was the gay one. (And quaint it was to listen to them, I remember, the King stammering in his Scots accent as if it hurt him to speak, and the Queen bubbling over in her French; and how they understood each other I could never make out.)

But Queen Marie [Henrietta Maria] had not come into Wales with the King. He had despatched her to her brother of France [Louis XIII] for her safety's sake when the civil strife grew hot, and she had enlivened neither his bed nor his board for a twelvemonth or more. And downcast indeed would he have been that sunny July of the year forty-five had he known that he would never have his way with her, nor ever see her more. For I verily believe he loved his wife more than his throne. A like mistake his son was resolved not to repeat.

I was aware, as were we all, that the King had grievous cause for anxiety. A month before he had witnessed his army put to the rout at Naseby fight, for though Prince Rupert had led the horse in a mad uphill charge and smashed Ireton's Roundheads opposed to 'em, the King's troops were outnumbered three to one, and Cromwell's Redcoats gave the Royal foot such a pounding that the poor King was compelled to concede the victory and to fly the field with the rebels in possession of all his guns and ammunition and stores. And his private cabinet of papers to boot. Not a man of the foot escaped; and more than a hundred of the officers' wives stripped and ravished and slashed in the face to mark them for life, and the soldiers' wives ill handled, too, and then knocked on the head and flung naked into the burial pits—the which is a shame and a crying-out against brute Cromwell and the Roundheads to the end of the world.

The defeated King had no notion where to turn for army or equipment or treasure again; and he came into Wales, among his loyalist subjects, in hopes that the clean and pleasant air would revive his drooping spirits and give him heart to renew the contest. He stayed mostly at Ragland Castle, but for one night he honoured my cousin, Richard Vaughan, Earl of Carbery, with his presence at Golden Grove in Carmarthenshire; and I had the honour of waiting upon his sacred Majesty.

To be sorry for the lonely and powerless King was one thing, to comfort him truly was quite another; but I served him at table humbly and demurely, though he had neither eyes nor thought for a serving wench, even one with Royal blood in her veins and many noble families in her cousinage. And it made me sad indeed to see him sitting there grave and silent, with no smile for a pretty maid and no welcoming ear for a singing boy's ballad; the while the young blades who attended him grew ever more loud and boastful in their cups.

His Majesty retired early to his devotions, and perhaps he gained more comfort from them than from aught else, the Queen being far away and beyond seas. And I slipped from the hall when he had gone, for it was not befitting my duty nor my state that I should serve anyone save the King; and the gallants who sat around the table could swagger the easier for my absence. Already had they conquered with their tongues in three Naseby fights.

I betook me to the shrubbery behind the house, where, in the coolth of the summer night, I could weep alone and unremarked. For I was but a young girl, and it was sad indeed to see a great and mighty King put down.

He had a steeper way still to fall, for nothing would appease brute Cromwell but the murder of his anointed King. But that was in the unseen future, and the present was unhappy enough. Sufficient unto that day was the evil thereof. Oft-times in my life have I wept over lesser tribulations, all unaware that greater misfortune was to come.

What augmented my melancholy, too, was that the Prince was not of the party. It had been noised abroad that he was to cross from Barnstaple to confer with his father at Golden Grove; but his place had been empty. My girlish fancy had been stirred at thought of renewing acquaintance; we had played together as babes, but for four years now he had been riding with the army, and at fifteen he counted as a man and a soldier blooded in many a fight. And I, too, of an age with him, knew full well that I was now a woman—innocent indeed, but plagued with thoughts of love.

Had I but known that the Prince's party rode up to the main door as I slipped out at the back, and that the King would not be roused from his prayers, even to greet his son, I had not lingered outside, you may be sure. Do not think that then I aspired to the love of the heir to the throne; but 'tis natural for young maids to dream romances, and wherever there is a young Prince there are maids to wonder if he may perchance cast an eye on them and love them. And my mirror told me what glances of men have very often confirmed—that I was lovely and that men must desire me.

And that night, indeed, as I wandered in the moonlight behind the great house, and dreamed my romantic dreams, and wept a little at the sadness of the world, I received unwelcome intimation that already men regarded me as a woman grown and meet for what the gallants call sport.

For one of the King's unwhipped escort, a young squire whose cheeks had neither known nor needed razor, but who had grown inches before manners, came out to relieve himself of the burden of my cousin Vaughan's wine, of which he had imbibed over-more than his capacity, in brain or body; and he spied me in the moonlight, though I stood still to avoid detection; and he strode towards me.

I made then to dodge into the bushes, but he had me by the shoulders before I could escape, and demanded why I wept, saying that if some lad had loved and left me I needed not to worry, there being other lads, and maybe better.

I told him that 'twas for the King I was grieving, and that I loved no lad, but wept because the King was quite undone and sorrowful, the which made me sad to think on't.

That he brushed aside, assuring me impatiently that the King would enjoy his own again, never fear, for the Redcoats would never stand against such soldiers as the King had now (meaning himself); and he bade me give him a kiss, and forget the King, for my pretty face was made for kisses, not tears.

But I had no mind to kiss him, nor for him to kiss me neither, for he was slobbery with wine, and his breath stank too, and his pawing hands made me sicken with disgust.

So I told him sharply enough that I was well aware that my lips were made for kissing, but that my kisses were for those that pleased me, and were not for the taking by any drunken knave.

To which he protested that he was no drunken knave, but a soldier, and sober enough to pick a pretty wench from a sour one.

I retorted that drunk or sober he would not pluck me; and I would not render up my lips to his neither, and I struggled to free myself from his lascivious grasp. But he was strong and lusty, and inflamed with desire too, and he clutched me round the shoulders so that my hands were imprisoned, or he had felt the weight of my palm on his cheek. I was not so young nor so innocent but I knew what was his intention, and I told him that I would never accept his counsel to forget the King, his master and mine, and to think only of him (my would-be ravisher), for methought he had a mind to give me what would cause me to remember him as long as I lived, aye, and to hate him as long as I lived too.

That, he could not deny and dared not affirm; so he said nought, but bussed my forehead and my ear and whatever of me he could reach with his slimy lips, and he tried to force my mouth up to his. But I kept my head down, and I swore to him that if he did not let me be, my cousin Vaughan would make him answer for it with his life.

He muttered that he cared not for twenty earls of Carbery, for he was a soldier, and would be riding away to-morrow, and to his death likely, and he thought it ill became a pretty maid who swore she loved the King and was loyal to him that she denied a favour to one that served the King with his sword, and with his life, too, maybe.

A favour such as he proposed to himself to take I could deny and I did. For as he shifted his hold to pull my chin up, and to tear at my dress, I wrenched my hand free, and I slapped him thrice on the cheek so that he let go altogether, and I slapped at him again, till he gripped my wrists, and then I bit his hand, for I was angry and I had thrown away the scabbard and would fight to the death to save my honour. Then he held me so that I could neither bite nor scratch; but he could do nought to me neither, so it was honours easy; and we wrestled and panted together. And I told him the sort of man I knew he was, and he quailed before my temper. For I am Welsh and my blood was up, and I was ever one to repel insult with my tongue. And he durst not let me free, though he had a mind to now, for he feared my nails would mark his smooth face, and 'tis not honourable for a soldier to have a wound that is not given by the enemy but by a slip of a wench that he tried to ravish and could not.

So I told him angrily that a youth who called himself a soldier would better serve the King by fighting his battles and destroying his enemies than by shaming the womenfolk of his loyal subjects. To which he had nought to say but to call me names, which were not true neither. For, said he, could I know what his intention was had I not suffered other men to do it to me?

And then a voice cut in on our contention, and never did more welcome voice soothe the ear of lady in distress! 'Twas not the voice of a full-grown man, but a treble, partly-broken, yet 'twas competent for its owner's purpose, too; for it spoke one sentence with a lazy drawl which hinted of laughter, and another with authority like the crack of a whip, commending my scornful speech for as true a speech as lass ever spoke, and then commanding the gallant to stand aside and let me be.

So concerned had we been in our tussle that we had not observed his approach; and he had grown so tall that I did not recognise His Royal Highness at the first; but my drunkard knew him on the instant, and sobered, and shrank back, releasing me. And in the sudden silence, as I looked at my rescuer, and it came over me that this was the Prince, I curtsied deep with humility and gratitude.

And then I perceived that my dress had torn down the front, and that I was all but naked to the waist, and both the Prince and my red-faced ravisher regarding me with more than common interest.

To attract the glances of men when a maid is in her finery to catch their eye is delight and satisfaction; but all I knew now was shame and anguish that they should behold my nakedness; and in my maiden confusion I pulled the tatters around my shoulders and turned to run away; but I tripped on my skirt, and fell headlong, and rolled over, and bumped my forehead; and I think I went into a swoon; for when I came to myself, the Prince was on one knee on the path, and I was reclining against his other knee, and his cloak around me, and he rubbing my forehead with his gentle hand.

I made to rise, protesting that his Royal Highness should not minister thus to me; but he dismissed my protest, saying soberly that he owned that 'twas his rudeness that had obliged me to run away, and therefore his fault that I had fallen, and his obligation to tend to my wounds. And then added, smiling, that he wished that the sight of his ugly face would make his father's enemies run, aye, and be more hurt when they fell.

Though 'twas his boyish stare that had led to my undoing, yet 'twas not his place to apologise to such as I, so I answered that my hurts were negligible and that I could well stand now, and walk too, and that I was grieved and ashamed to have put him to such trouble; but he insisted that 'twas for him to apologise to me in that one of his father's servants had molested me.

The fellow had slunk away, and I never saw him again; what his punishment was I know not, for the Prince promised to punish him, tho' I protested he had done me no harm; but when I asked him one day in Paris whether he had hanged the lout or whatever, he laughed merrily and answered that 'twould have been ingrateful in him to have hanged the benefactor that showed him how beautiful I was, for, Faith! he deserved promotion! And when I pressed, for I was not vindictive and I hoped he had not been sorely punished for what he did in his cups, the Prince swore he could not remember. So perhaps all the charge the lad was put to for his drunken frolic was the money the Prince made him leave with my cousin Vaughan to buy me a new dress. And death, sword in hand, hath been his portion belike, long since.

But I come back to my story and my Prince. There was I resting trustful in his arms on the path, with my face upturned to his, and him bending over me, and I thought that if he had a mind to steal a kiss he was welcome and more than welcome to take all he desired of me.

And I think the same thought was with him, too, for he held me there, which was comfortable enough for me, but I doubt not miscomfortable for him; but he was a tall lad and strong, and a lad can endure discomfort when he holds a pretty wench in his arms and she is smiling up at him and awaiting his desires.

But he did not kiss me at once, for he was shy, since (he told me this later, in Paris) he had not kissed a maid before; his thoughts for years had been of war and fighting and marches and sieges, and of taking life away rather than of making new lives. Moreover, but five minutes before he had seen me repel with vigour an attack on my maiden lips, and, though he was the Prince, he maybe doubted that I would surrender to him what I had so angrily denied to another. So he hesitated, and maintained his advantageous position the while he marshalled his resolution for the advance.

And since to gaze in silence into a maid's eyes and not to meet her closely lip to lip is but tedious and tantalising for a lusty young man, he began to converse to pass the time and hide his irresolution. And I was content that he should, for though, had he pressed me, I had yielded all, yet I did not think he intended to do me a mischief.

So he enquired who I was; and when I told him I was Lucy Walter, and that my father was William Walter of Roch Castle, Pembrokeshire (burnt, the year before, by my cousin Rowland Laugharne on brute Cromwell's orders), and that my mother's mother, Eleanor Vaughan, was aunt to his host, my cousin Richard Vaughan, second Earl of Carbery, he graciously acknowledged that he remembered me very well; and he recalled the days before the civil strife, when we played childish games together at his father's palace. To which I said that I supposed we should never play such games together again; and he said that perhaps there were grown-up games we could play at some more convenient season. To which I said, with all my heart. And he said, with all his too. And so we were honours easy; and we fell sudden silent, for we neither of us knew what to say next; and though he no doubt knew what to do, he was struck shy and could not do it.

So presently he said that he remembered me as a merry little girl, with brown hair and saucy eyes and a Welsh lilt to my voice, and a Welsh temper to my tongue; and he went on to say that, Faith! from what he had seen and heard that night, I was still a merry little girl with brown hair and saucy eyes and a Welsh lilt to my voice and a Welsh temper to my tongue, and a smarting right hand too.

To which I replied that, as I was of an age with him, and he was now a man and a soldier, so I was now a woman; and that though I had not put aside my Welsh tongue, no, nor my Welsh temper neither, nor never would, yet I promised him that never should my loyalty allow me to direct my Welsh-tempered tongue at his Royal Highness, for he had rescued me in my hour of peril.

He allowed that 'twas indeed a pretty speech, and one that he would remember; and so, growing bolder, he asked did I intend indeed to reserve my kisses for those on whom I would bestow them, for he doubted I would succeed in restricting my favours so, since so handsome a wench as I would never want for gallants eager to pluck what I might not desire to surrender, nor yet have the strength to defend. To which I replied that I was afeared he had the right of it, and that therefore the fortress of my maiden lips must needs strike when the conquering commander appeared.

He repeated the words, 'the conquering commander', musingly, trying to imitate my Welsh voice, with his eyes twinkling; and I explained to him, primly enough, that a loyal Welsh woman was necessarily at a disadvantage when she found herself trapped in the arms of the Prince of Wales.

He could have no doubts of me then, for he stopped my mouth with his lips, and I tasted for the first time the joys of a true lovers' kiss. At least, I was necessitated to love him from that time forth (as I love him still and shall always love him, illtreat me as he will); and it seemed that he loved me in return.

But there is such magic in the kisses of Princes that they breed illusion in an innocent maid's mind, and perhaps he did not love me at all, but was only enjoying the novelty of his first embrace.

And if, as he swore to me afterwards in Paris, I was the first maid he ever kissed (as he was in truth the first and only man ever to kiss me loverlike on the lips), he was clearly a man made for kissing, he took to it so naturally.

How long we kissed thus, I cannot tell, for I lay in comfort and delight; but Princes are not accustomed to stooping on bended knee; and at last he helped me to my feet, and folded his cloak around my shoulders—for as I arose, it slipped off on to the ground and again I was half-naked before him, and not ashamed neither, for I knew that I loved him and was his for ever. But he was shy still, and if he could not guess that I was at his mercy, 'twas not my part to tell him so.

He stamped his feet and rubbed his leg, for it ached, he said, from bending in one position so long; and he said with a sigh that he must surely be about his business. The which, I suppose, reminded him what his business was; for he made me promise that I should never reveal to a soul that he was with his father the King on that day and in that place, for he said that the meeting was secret, and his father's Kingdom depended on it, and he trusted me as a loyal subject to keep the fact close. Which I always have until this day, although it cannot matter now, and why it should have been so plaguey a secret I never could understand; nor how it could be kept secret neither when such boasting bully-boys as attended the King knew of it.

The Prince offered me his arm to return to the house, and as we walked thereto, he said musingly that heretofore, when a man under his command had jumped his duty to dally with a maid, he had been stern with him—and unkind too, he now perceived—for he had not understood what delights the man had been required to forego. For the future, he vowed, he would be more understanding, for Mistress Lucy's sake.

But I told him that, though he might be more understanding, he should not be less stern; for his father's cause, and his own, too, ought not to wait upon dalliance.

I could bear to remind him of that, though my heart ached; for never was maidenhead more ripe for the harvesting than mine at that moment, and never was maiden more distressed to retain her honour. And I knew not then that we should ever meet again.

His thoughts must have coincided with mine, for as we halted at the door, he said that we should meet again, and then added with determination that 'twas imperative we meet again, but when, he knew not, for he was necessitated to be aboard ship and halfway to the coast of Devon before dawn; and when he should see the Welsh mountains and hear Welsh voices again might be far in the future.

(And, indeed, I think he has not set foot in the most lovely of all lands from that day to this, though he gazed long at the blue distances of Radnor during his retreat from Worcester fight. When he has his throne again, he will visit Wales, and Pembrokeshire especially, and Golden Grove, too, and take me with him; he has promised me that.)

So I kissed his hand in the doorway; and suddenly he slipped a ring from his finger, and gave it to me with the injunction to wear it as a pledge that we should meet again, or use it as a token to send him should I desire his aid. So dumbfounded was I at his generosity that I had scarce wit enough to unwrap from his cloak and hand it to him; and to curtsey to him was clean out of my mind; but somehow I gathered my rags around me and scampered up the broad stairs, like I was a child again. But on the landing I halted and turned and looked down on him.

Charles was a fine figure of a lad, even then, for he was tall and black, with a brown skin and black curling hair and thick eyebrows; he was every inch of two yards a Prince, and very handsome and of a regal bearing, and I loved him with all my heart. Which is the picture I have carried in my mind's eye for ever after—my Prince gazing up at me and smiling.

And then he waved his hand, and strode off to my Lord's room, with his cloak over his arm and his fine feathered hat on his head.

In the morning, my Prince was gone (and so was the King and the fellow who had brought us together); within a twelvemonth he had gone beyond sea, and it was the most of three years before I beheld him again.

And that (said Mistress Barlow) is the story of all that passed between Prince Charles Stuart of Wales and myself when we met at Golden Grove in Carmarthenshire that evening in July, in the year of our Lord sixteen hundred and forty-five. 'Tis the true story as I hope to be saved. 'Twas a fateful meeting, for it led to my ruin and my shame. What sprung from it was great joy and great sorrow. It was the first step on the path to where I now confess repentance for my sin.

II England: The King's Treasure

(Winter 1647-8)

I HAVE TOLD you (said Mistress Barlow) how I met and loved
the Prince of Wales when I was abiding with my cousin, my
Lord Carbery, at Golden Grove in County Carmarthen, in July
of the year forty-five. The reason why I was at Golden Grove and
not with my parents was that my mother and my father had
fallen out some years since, and were contesting at push of pike
at law, and my mother had not the wherewithal to support me
and my brothers too, so my cousin Vaughan invited me to make
my home with him until I should find me a husband. But after
I had met the Prince of Wales I did not think any more of a
husband, for I dreamed of no husband but the Prince. How
could I submit my lips and my body to a lesser man when I
had lain content and eager in his arms?

The law-suit between my father and my mother dragged on
many years; for the law's delays were many during the civil
strife, and my mother resided in London and he in Wales. He
had carried us all to London when I was eight, and we lodged
in the back side of Covent Garden; but in forty-one he returned
to Haverfordwest, leaving my mother and me and my two
brothers in London. He had a whore in Haverford, she had been
a serving-maid to my mother, and he got her with child, and
desired my mother to bring up the child with hers lawfully

13

begotten, which she would not. And it was this whore of his, as
well as my mother's portion and maintenance, that the law-suit
was about. And though my mother had a lien on his rents, she
oft-times could not collect 'em, and had it not been for the
charity of her sisters and her mother she and we had starved.

My mother was truly loyal to the King, but my father cared
for naught but money, and when he saw brute Cromwell come
out on top, he was forward to cry up Parliament and to
ingratiate himself with the rebels, and he cozened the Roundhead House of Lords by naming my mother as malignant, which
was the word they had for loyal, and so he won the day against
my mother; for the outcome of the law-suit was that my mother
should not receive a penny more from his rents, and that his
children must go home to him to provide for their keeping and
education. A most monstrous decision this was, for it meant
that his children lawfully begotten were to be at the beck and
call of his whore and at her mercy for their provisioning and
apparel. He cared nothing for his legitimate children, and his
only desire to have us live with him was, that he should triumph
over my mother.

My brothers went back to Wales, for Richard was a Roundhead at heart (and indeed he served Cromwell as High Sheriff
of Pembrokeshire a year or two since) and Justus is the scholar of
the family and wanted learning and my father promised to put
him to study law, which he did.

But when my father wrote that I must go and keep house for
him at Haverford, I said I would not, not for Cadwallader and
all his goats, for he had a serving-wench there who could keep
house for him more competently than I could, seeing she understood his needs, and could serve him in a manner a daughter
could not. And when he threatened to send the Sheriff to drag
me there by force, I told him to tell the Sheriff to pluck some
drab from a ditch that would serve my father more willing than
I; and I hid myself with my grand-dam at St Giles in the Fields,
which is not in London, but nearby, so that you could walk into
London when you willed, and smell London whether you willed

or no. And so that the Sheriff should have the more trouble to find me, I gave out that my name was Lucy Protheroe, which was my mother's name before her marriage.

But I was at a loss to know what to do then, for I was not minded to take a husband, and indeed no man would be forward to take me without a portion, which my father would not give me and my mother could not.

So I wrote a letter to the Prince and sent it to him by a trusted messenger I knew of, and I told him how I was fixed, and I reminded him of his promise that we should meet again, and I begged him to find me a place in attendance on his mother the Queen; and I said I would gladly come to Paris if I could find the wherewithal to live honestly there, in howsoever menial a capacity.

He did not answer me by letter, for that would have endangered me, and the messenger, too, belike; and I thought he had forgotten me, for 'twas two years since we had met at Golden Grove; but one morning, when I strolled in the Broad Walk of Paul's [St Paul's Cathedral] bemoaning that I wanted the money to purchase the ribbons displayed there, a dirty beggar-man with a patch over his eye and a stump for a leg plucks me by the sleeve and asks if I be Mistress Lucy Walter from Golden Grove.

I was afeared to concede that I was, in case he was the Sheriff's man from my father, yet I did not like to deny it neither, in case 'twas a summons from the Prince, so I replied by asking what he would say if I was. To which he whispered that if indeed I was Mistress Walter, which he truly suspected me to be, then he was to tell me that someone who remembered Golden Grove, but naming no names, had received my petition and had hopes that I might be able to serve that someone mightily, and that he was concerned in the business of finding me the place I had spoke of. To which I said that I was sorry for the beggar's misfortunes, but that I could give him nothing for I had nothing, but that if I met him again when I had money I should be glad to give him something for his comfort. And he pulled his forelock and muttered out loud that, sure, we should meet again; and indeed we did, and I gave him sixpence.

'Twas a month or more before my impatience to hear from the Prince was rewarded, and then it was from my aunt Gosfright that I learned what was toward. She is my mother's sister Margaret, who was married to a Dutch merchant, Peter Gosfright by name, of St Dunstans in the West, but he is dead now. It was by a ship's master that letters were sent to the Court at St Germain, and my uncle Gosfright passed 'em to a merchant in Rouen, one Sambourne, though my uncle did not understand the cipher they were written in, but my aunt Gosfright did.

One afternoon in the autumn my aunt Gosfright comes to us at St Giles and asks me to walk with her in the fields, and when we are come towards Mary-le-bone and there is no one nearby to hear what she says, she informs me that if I have a mind to go for Paris, the which she knows well I have, I can be of great service to the King if I will take in my charge some articles which are needed at the Court. To which I reply that I will be very willing to do all I can for the King and the Queen and the Prince.

My aunt Gosfright says that the mission will be dangerous, and that only a messenger who is devoted and trusted and honest will suffice for the business; only it must be someone the Parliament men will not suspect, which is why it is thought I might do it, if I would. To which I say that I would give my life, if not for the King, at least for the Prince of Wales.

My aunt Gosfright smiles at that, and says she does not conceive the Parliament would hang me were I captured, but they would certainly clap me up in prison; and, what would be worse for the King's cause would be that they would take away whatever it was I was carrying to the Queen and it would be lost.

I say I would risk prison and worse, though I know I would like as not die of fever in some stinking jail, but 'twould be for the King and the Prince; and I am impatient to know what it is I am to do.

(Now the curious thing was that 'twas not I who was put in prison in respect of the business, but my aunt Gosfright; but that was long after I came to France, when some traitor turned informer; and my aunt did not die in prison, but is still alive in London.)

When I said I was impatient to know what I had to do to serve the King, my aunt looked at me narrowly, and asked if I would cut off my curls and black my face and travel to France as a young blackamoor; and I hesitated at that, for my curls were lovely (as you can see they are still), and my skin was soft and pink, though now it is not so fresh as it was then; and I asked if I was to present myself to the Prince thus; and my aunt laughed and said that if I did he would not recognise me, so I need not be afeared he would not love me when my curls grew again. Indeed, did I carry the business through, and deliver the things he wanted, he would be sure to love me. And so I said I hoped I should never want the courage and resolution to serve the King and the Queen and the Prince in whatever guise it pleased them for me to adopt.

So it was fixed that I would carry out the business, but my aunt Gosfright could not tell me what it was I was to transport across seas to the Court, nor when nor how I was to go; and I fretted for several weeks before I heard another word. And, indeed, I was to fret for some months, for the plot kept a-changing, and the disguise I was to wear changed with the party I was to sail with, so that sometimes I was to be a boy, and sometimes a serving-wench, and once I was to be an old woman, but most of the time I was to be a little black moor attending some rich lady. In truth, as I understood later, it was a desperate business I was to be mixed up in; it wanted ten or a dozen bold and silent men to carry out the design, and two of 'em had to be tailors, and one a locksmith, and 'twas hard to find such men with the Parliament spies all about everyone who was thought to favour the cause of the captive King.

But in the end all came well. 'Twas at the beginning of March, in the year forty-eight, that my aunt Gosfright told me that the business was to go through, and that I was to travel as a poor country boy and not as a black one, which pleased me mightily, for I had been distressed to think that if I went to France as a black boy I might not be able to wash off all the black before the Prince saw me.

My aunt tells me that what I must do is to give out that I am resolved to go into Pembrokeshire to my father, so that he would give me a portion and find me a husband, for I am rising eighteen now and it is high time I am married and put in the way of producing the next generation. So I am to go into London with my box very early one morning and take it to a house on the back side of Poultry, where I can join a merchant who is proceeding into Wales, and so travel with him and his family. This is what I am to say to my grand-dam's neighbours at St Giles, so that my departure can be accounted for.

But when I get myself to the back side of Poultry on the day appointed, there is no merchant there, and no coach neither, but only the beggar-man with the patch over his eye and the old soldier's leg; and he signs to me to follow him, and leads me along an alleyway to a low door which he bids me enter, and inside there are two brisk plump matrons who take me upstairs and ask me my name and what is the title of Richard Vaughan and where his estate is; and when I say my name is Lucy Walter, and Richard Vaughan is the second Earl of Carbery and his estate is Golden Grove in Carmarthenshire, they say that in that case I must have my curls cut off so that I can be clad as a short-haired boy. The which they proceed to do, and I bear the operation with fortitude, though I weep when I see my cropped head in the mirror afterwards.

Then they bade me take off all my clothes, which I did till I stood up naked and trembling before them, wearing nothing at all but the Prince's ring, and with my hair cropped close like a Roundhead's. And they kept me standing there, ashamed and shivering and afeared and yet excited, while they debated, the one with t'other, how to tie up my bosom with a bandage so that it was flat. First they try one way and then another, taking no notice of me and chattering as if I was a capon they were trussing up for the pot; but finally they find a method that satisfies them, but which distresses me, for though it does not pain me, yet I am afeared that if I have to keep myself tied up so for a week or more, which they say I have to, I shall not be able to come back to my proper shape again afterwards; but they only laugh at my fears and assure me that by the time I have given suck to half-a-dozen whelps, which they each said they had, I shall have a bosom I can be proud of, as they say they are of theirs, though to tell the truth I prefer my own before they bound it up, the which I tell them with some spirit, but they only giggle, and say, why, a bosom that has not given suck is no bosom at all.

Then they dressed me in a coarse boy's shirt, which was dirty, and a pair of old breeches, and two pairs of woollen stockings to thicken my legs, and clumsy boy's shoes, and a leather jerkin, and clapped a greasy old hat on my head, and turned me from one to the other to admire the effect, and laughed in their bawdy way, and assured me that maybe I could pass for a boy so long as I kept my hat pulled down over my face and never went out of doors except on a dark night.

Which disappointed me mightily so that I began to weep, for I thought that, if the enterprise depended on my passing for a boy, 'twas bound to fail; but they cheered me by asserting that if I dirtied my face and hands and pared my nails close, I would pass muster in the company I was to keep.

One of 'em suggests that my disguise will be impenetrable if they pull out one of my front teeth, so that I can present a gap-tooth grin to the world, and t'other is inclined to agree with her; but when they see I am about to weep again at so much sacrifice of my beauty, they give over their merry joking, and pronounce me ugly enough as I am.

But when I asked them when I was going and where and who with, they protested that they did not know exactly, for 'twas integral to the business that no one should know all; but I was to wait in that room and accustom myself to wearing boy's garments (but not to allow myself to be seen at the window), until I was sent for, which would be in a day or two. With which I had to be content.

They brought me ale and victuals and a rug; and they took away my box and my own garments, saying I should have them at the end of my journey, wherever that might be; and though I doubted this, I durst not protest. I had put myself into the hands of plotters and desperate persons and must do what I was told and submit to my fate, for I understood well that all who were concerned in the enterprise staked their liberties if not their lives, and the less any one knew of the affairs of t'others the safer for us all.

So they went out and locked the door and left me alone, and I sat there in alarm and impatience all day, not knowing whether the end of my journey would be the caresses of the Prince or the tickling straw of a jail, or perhaps a bared-back whipping from the public executioner or my father; for I did not know who the devil's hands I was in; and I wept a little at thought that perhaps the business would come to naught and my curls had been raped to no avail; but I felt the Prince's ring pressing against my toe (where the women had made me hide it in my shoe), and I trusted to him (not knowing then, as I know now, what a big fool a wench is who trusts to him), and when it came dark, I wrapped myself in the rug and fell asleep.

But not for long. And if you conceive that an innocent maid, setting out to travel beyond seas at the beckoning of the Prince she loves will dream of his kisses, you are wrong; for the dream I had was of a rough-handed coarse butcher of a man stripping off my dress, so that he could tie me to the tree for a whipping; but when I awake all in a muck-sweat and crying out in terror, I find it is one of the women pulling the rug away to rouse me.

She says I am to start in an hour, and I must be silent and make haste. I am very willing to leave that house, but first I must take off my jerkin and shirt and encase my body in a great stiff belt of flannel on the inside and leather on the outside, which covers all my waist and belly and fills me up from my bosom on one side to my backside on t'other, so that it disguises my shape completely and renders me a stout fellow indeed; and when I don shirt and jerkin again no one can suspect I am a wench by the figure of me.

And indeed, I could not feel myself to be a wench neither, with my bosom tied up flat and this thick wide belt encompassing my middle. Under the leather, it felt hard in places, and though I was strictly enjoined that I was neither to ask nor to guess what was sewn in it, yet I knew 'twas not papers, and I doubted not from these lumps and the weight of the thing, that I was carrying on my person a fortune in jewels and precious stones. 'Twas indeed a part of the royal treasure, which had been left in London when the King rode away to raise forces in forty-one, and it had been filched from the Tower the night previous by some desperate adherents of the King with the connivance of two of the guards; and two nimble-fingered tailors had employed the whole day sewing the jewels into the belt so that it would be well distributed and would not shake nor rattle; and though I did not know this at the time, yet I suspected that my burden was some treasure that was stolen (as the Parliament would regard it), and that there would be a hue and cry after it. But though I was afeared of the consequences of being cotched with it, and had no relish to be stripped naked by rude soldiery, yet I was not hindered in my resolution to proceed with the enterprise. For 'twas for the Prince.

When I was dressed again, the good wife suddenly kissed me and said I was a proper young fellow and if she was but twenty years younger her virtue would be mine for the asking; and then she smacked me smartly on the rump and bade me be off and do the same to the Prince of Wales when I met him. And so pushed me down the stairs and into a courtyard, where was a lumbering old farm cart, with a pile of empty sacks in it, and two sturdy country fellows, ready to drive off.

One hoisted me into the back of the cart and climbed up after me, and we lay on some sacks and pulled others over us for warmth and protection from the rain; and the other got into the driver's seat, and so we set out, jolting over the slippery cobble-stones of London, in the cold and wet of the middle of the night, with no word spoken, save those the driver mumbled to the horse.

So I began my journey to the West Country, with my hair sheared short, and in boy's clothes, with a King's ransom strapped to my belly, trusting my life and my honour to two poor men whom I had never heard of nor seen before, and whose names I did not know. They told me to call the tall one Ben and the short one John, but these were not their names neither.

We were fifteen days together, the three of us, for we did not travel straight, and we avoided roads and towns when we could, going zig-zag from friend to friend, so that we could be provided with guides and victuals and news of Roundhead soldiers that might be searching for a treasure which some desperate villains had stolen from the Tower. Only we never mentioned treasure, and whether those who helped us knew who we were and what our business was, I never did discover. For we kept very close about it, and all we allowed was that we were friends of the King; and that was enough. And, faith! often I marvelled at the number of poor men and women who were loyal to the captive King, and would risk lives and liberty and property in his service.

We adopted all manner of stratagems to baffle pursuit; sometimes we carted a load of produce or dung from one farm to another; and sometimes we lay up all day and tramped across the heath-land by night. And we altered our garb, too, leaving behind at houses where we lodged the jackets we had come in, and facing the next day's wind and rain in different cuts and colours. Only I never parted with the belt, nor suffered anyone to see it neither.

Many of those who helped us on our way I never did see, nor they me, for oft-times Ben or John would go forward to a farm to enquire could they accommodate us, while t'other man and I lay up in a thicket; and if they would have us, then we went to a barn or outhouse and kept close there, and some-

times no one came nigh, for the fewer persons who saw us and
could describe us if interrogated by the Roundheads, the safer
for us all. But other times we went into houses and were greeted
there (so that once I slept in a bed—but not comfortable because
of the belt); and once, when the soldiers were in the neighbour-
hood, 'twas decided there was nothing for it but I should lay
up two whole days in the squire's priests' hole, whilst John and
Ben went boldly back and forth among the soldiers as the squire's
labourers. I was greatly afeared as I lay crouched in that priests'
hole, waiting for the secret door to be broken down any hour,
for I thought the Puritans knew all the secret parts of Catholic
houses; but they did not know this one. I was right glad to
emerge safe, and I think there never was stranger priest in that
closet, nor in any other neither, than a maid with her hair shorn
short, and her face dirtied, and her bosom tied up, and dressed
as a boy with a fortune in jewels belted against her belly.

'Twas a great puzzle to me at first, and a matter of considerable interest, whether the good folk we trusted with our liberty,
and who saw me and spoke with me, knew that I was a woman
and not the boy I was dressed for. But afterwards I became
bolder, for everywhere I was accounted a boy, and became habited
to being treated as a runabout by the men who were our guides.
And once our guide was a maid no older than myself, who cast
sheeps' eyes at me all morning, and would have me buss her
at parting, which I did heartily enough, and slapped her backside
too, and whispered that if ever I came that way when I was
a grown man I would seek her out and demonstrate to her the
man I was, which I have never done because I have never passed
that way again, though I doubt that she is waiting for me still,
for so saucy a wench must have found a proper fellow to do her
business for her long since, and she's been wedded and bedded,
too, no doubt, and is the mother of saucy boys herself.

My companions knew I was no youth, though they knew not
my name nor more of my state than that I was of gentle birth,
and they made ways smooth for me when they could without
risk to us all, by letting me ride in the comfortablest seat and

sleep on the softest bed—which was oft-times a truss in a hay-loft—and they reserved for me the choicest morsels of our rough food, and treated me with proper deference when no one was by. But when we were like to be observed, I became but a boy to them, and I must assist them unload carts and push at the wheels when they were stuck in ruts and mud, and fetch and carry for them, and do all manner of noisome work which a boy travelling with men would be put to. So that my hands became rough as a real boy's, and my garments bemired; and my face was always dirty.

For public show, sometimes, they boxed my ears (though never hard), for boys are better, they said, for having their ears boxed; and they cursed me and threatened me with beatings for not running fast enough to do their bidding, and oft-times I was hard put to it to keep my temper and not flare up at them, for I was ever one to resent an insult and to answer word for word and blow for blow, and had it not been within my boy's part to be saucy, I had not upheld the masquerade. For 'twas all play-acting, and we laughed at it in private, and I did not bear malice for their buffets and their curses, but enjoyed 'em, for they were playing their parts as I was playing mine, and I endured it all for the King's sake and the Prince's; and were it not for my poor feet, which were cruelly chafed and blistered by the heavy shoes, and my poor body, so stiff and sweated beneath the heavy belt, I had been happier those two weeks than at any time in my life, almost. For though I was tired often, and hungry often, and athirst often, and afeared often, and dirty and footsore always, and had my hair shorn—aye, and carried straws and lice in it, too—yet I was on the Prince's important business, and every weary step took me nearer to him.

And as for dressing in a boy's garments and displaying my legs to all the world, why, I thought nought of that after the first day, for though 'tis immodest in a maid to allow men to observe her legs, yet mine are well-shaped legs and comely, and to display 'em was essential to my part, and I did not feel like a maid whiles I bore the great belt round me. In one thing, though, John and Ben did not treat me as a boy; for they did nothing to offend my modesty, and they minded not that I went apart for my needs, and they went out of sight for their own, though men we travelled with did not, which helped me to be confident in my disguise. Yet sometimes I was afeared our guides might wonder that a boy should flinch from relieving himself in the ditch alongside the men; and once a farmer whose barn we lay in came round a corner and caught me with my breeches down before I was aware of him; but if he saw aught, he said nought. He was a loyal King's man and knew the value of a shut mouth.

So everywhere I passed for a boy, or at least received a boy's treatment. Once I had my ears boxed right smartly by an ostler at an inn; and once a coachman slashed at me with his whip by reason that I did not leap out of his way fast enough,—and, faith! burdened as I was with this belt, I could not leap for my life's sake; and I carried a weal across my face all the way to France.

But I kept away from strange men all I could, for if one touched my body he might feel the belt and some hard lumps in it, and then we might be discovered, and lose all. It was indeed my perpetual worry; for if it should be suspected by some rough fellows that I was a maid and had treasure on my person, my companions would be hard put to it to protect me, and if they failed, we would be undone, for the King would lose his jewels and I my maidenhead.

I think that one reason why I could pass for a rough boy was that I am Welsh and people who speak in a Welsh voice are uncommon in the South country, but are common enough to be recognised as such; and as the Welsh voice is a musical sing-ing voice with women and men alike, sure the folk who heard me speak could not perceive whether I was girl or treble-voiced boy or hovel-born or gentlefolk. And so I passed for what I was not.

What confirmed me in this opinion was, that at an inn where we lay one night, as I came into the courtyard in the morning,

a loutish boy was in my way, and when I asked him, politely
enough, that I might pass, he answered, seizing on my Welsh
voice, that he would not do it, no, not for Cadwallader and all
his goats. To which I replied that to be sure he would do it for
King Cadwallader briskly enough, and that Cadwallader was one
of my ancestors (which is true, too). But he said he doubted I
was descended from King Cadwallader, though I might come
from one of his goats. At which I made to slap him, but then
methought that, being a boy, I must hit him with my closed
fist, but I had not the way of it, so I stood foolish, with my
hand raised, fearful lest I reveal myself by a womanish gesture.
But luckily the boy was more afeared than I, and he misliked
my fierce movement, so he poked his tongue out at me and
made off quickly.

We were only in serious danger but twice. Once was when
we came sudden upon a party of Roundhead Redcoats resting by
the roadside one high noon, and the officer made us halt and
interrogated us narrowly as to who we were and whence we
came and whither we were bound; to all of which my companions gave glib answers, and produced a paper too which had
been provided them against such an event, and which the officer
could not gainsay.

But he is not satisfied, neither, for he stares fierce at me, and
presently bids me come close (for I am skulking in the back-
ground and saying nought), and asks what my name is, and
when I tell him it is David Jones (for such was the name I went
by), he grips me by the arm and demands why a Welsh boy
should be tramping in Hants with Kentish men. So I tell him
my father was Welsh and my mother of Kent, who had gone
to Wales as a serving-woman with my lord of Leicester, and met
my father there and married him, but that both are dead, so I
am come home to be with my uncle. 'Tis a pretty story, and
I can tell him more, too (for my lord of Leicester is my cousin
and I know his family too); but he swears an oath such as is
not seemly in a member of an army of Saints, and says there
may be some truth in it, but he doubts that my mother married

my father, or I had been a more likely-looking lad, for though I seemed plump enough about the body, the muscles of my arms were weak as a girl's; to which I stammer that my parents had been very poor, and we had eaten meat but once a year, at harvest time. All the while, I am afeared he will poke my body with his finger, and discover the belt, but he does not, only bids me be on my way, and swings me round sudden, and aims a kick at me which catches me square on the backside and sends me sprawling in the ditch; and all the Roundheads laugh like dripping gutters for reason that I do not jump up quickly, but roll over in the ditch, because I am not able to bend easily in the belt.

So when I clamber to my feet, I demonstrate my pretended sex by making a rude gesture to the soldiers, at which my pretended uncle proffers me such a whirret across the cheek for my incivility that I land head first in the ditch again.

The soldiers marched off satisfied enough, for they had had sport with me; but they would have laughed the other side of their sour faces had they ever learned the reason for my clumsiness—to say nought of the sport these godly men would have had with the poor maid had her true sex been uncovered.

The second time we were in danger was a desperate business indeed, though I never could understand exactly what danger we were in, nor my companions neither. 'Twas a night full of the moon, and the three of us were trudging westwards across the great upland heath that is in those parts. So clear a night was it that we had seen in the distance the old upstanding stones that the men told me was called Stone-Henge, but we did not go nigh it, and we made for the lower ground, where there was a chance of a hedge or a ditch to shelter us from distant viewers.

But while we were out on the open plain, we heard a horse galloping behind us, and, as there was no place to hide, we marched on like honest folk, expecting the horseman would pass by on his own business. But he did not, but circled round us, and reined in, facing us menacing, and demanding who we were, and why we were abroad at dead of night.

His voice was high, so that I judged him to be but a youth, but his clothes and accoutrement were costly, and he handled his horse with skill. Yet he was impetuous and foolish and over-confident, too, for he broke in on Ben's story and denied it roundly, and when John sought to corroborate it, he roughly bade him hold his tongue, for he knew we were rogues and thieves, and we must accompany him into Salisbury, to be lodged in the jail until morning, when we could answer for ourselves to the colonel there.

And when my companions said we would not, for we were honest men on lawful business, he whipped out his sword and made a cut at Ben, who dealt him such a blow across the forearm with his stave that he dropped the sword, which John caught as it fell, and when the foolish youth pulled out a pistol as if to aim it at us, John drove the sword up under his short ribs, so that he fell from his horse and was dead before he hit the ground.

I had seen dead men a-plenty in the streets of London, and men slain, too, in street brawls, but never had I seen a man die so sudden and so surprised at what had happened to him. For he screamed, and gasped once, and was in the presence of his Maker.

And as he lay on his back in the moonlight, with his hat fallen off, 'twas evident he was barely weaned from his mother's milk, for his cheek was as smooth as mine, and his hair as long and silky as any fine lady's. Had he not attempted to ape the man, and assume an authority he could not support, he had lived to grow into a man one day, perhaps.

My two companions debated what to do, and I said nothing, for I was in their hands and was content to abide by their decision: which was, to despoil the lad of his finger-rings and his purse, and the gold locket and chain which was round his neck and which had a yellow-haired lass's picture in it—so that it should be thought by those that found him that he had been set upon and murdered by robbers; and then to hide his body and weapons as best they might; and bury the trinkets some-

wheres else, so that we should not have them on our persons
were we apprehended.

So they carried the body to a ditch near by, and flung him
in face downwards, and trampled him deep in the mud, and
covered him with a few branches, so that he might not be found
unless by one searching for him; and the ornaments they buried
under a tree in a wood we came to presently. The money they
kept, for 'twas not so much as to be suspicious; they offered me
a share, but I declined it; and I hope they dug up the gold
later and had the value of it for their pains.

As for the mare, she had trotted off, and no doubt returned
to her stable to set up a hue and cry for her master the next day,
but of that we heard nought.

So the foolish would-be man who had challenged two stout
soldiers so impetuously and with such fire and confidence but
half an hour before, we left stamped face downwards in the mud
of a lonely ditch, his gay coat stained with his heart's blood, and
his silken curls matted and sodden. And who he was, and what
his business was to be abroad at so late an hour, and why he
attempted to arrest us, and whether his body was ever found,
I do not know to this day.

No doubt the golden-haired lass wept when she learned of
his fate; as indeed I wept myself when I thought of him after
the shock of combat had passed off.

My companions made reference to the murder but once, when
Ben remarked, in apology to me, as I supposed, that in a battle,
if a man puts a pistol to your head, you may not hesitate, but
must strike as fatal a blow as you can, for 'tis your life or his;
to which I replied that though it grieved me to see a young life
taken, yet I realised there was no help for it, and that many
young and valiant men died so, one side or the other, in the
late war. And John said that just so had young Charles Caven-
dish, my lord of Devonshire's son, been slain at the fight at
Gainsborough with Cromwell's men in the summer of forty-
three; for he was there and saw it happen.

There was nothing for it but to thank Ben and John for so

doughtily preserving the King's treasure and my liberty; and thus the matter ended and we did not speak of it again. Indeed, it imported little to them; for they were soldiers, and had slain men in battle, and had been slain themselves had they not been quick and resolute to get their blows in first. And I did not look upon them as murderers, for the youth had died in fair fight provoked by himself; it was in defence of the King's jewels, for had we not defied him, we had been quite undone.

Ben and John were rough men, yet they were loyal subjects of the King and honest servants of the Protestant Church; and they treated me kindly, and protected me, and the King has promised that when he comes into his own again he will seek them out and reward them.

The last two days we lay up in the barns of friendly farmers, and then tramped over the hills of Dorsetshire by night; and on the early morning of the fifteenth day we came down the steep hill into Lyme, and I found my uncle Barlow awaiting me in a house by the Cobb. It was here Ben and John left me, and I never saw them again.

My uncle Barlow was impatient, not only for the success of the whole desperate enterprise, but also for my safety. A swifter messenger had brought him my box, and had informed him of my departure from London; since when he had heard nought of me; and he had lain nearly a month at Lyme, fearful of being discovered every day, for he did not trust the woman he lodged with, though she proved faithful. He was a brave man, I knew, but as the affair approached its consummation so did the risk of failure increase, and his anxiety with it.

I should explain that John Barlow of Slebech is my uncle by marriage, having married one of my mother's sisters; he has been loyal always to the King, and his estate had been confiscated by Parliament and granted to our black-hearted cousin, Rowland Laugharne, no doubt as a reward for burning down my father's castle of Roch when it had been garrisoned for the King by my lord Carbery. My uncle Barlow had been taken prisoner at Fort Pill, but was free again, and eager to serve the

King on any desperate venture. So the plan was that he should come to Lyme and escort me and the treasure across to France.

'Tis an agreeable town, Lyme, and one I have an affection for, by reason of the fact that I came to it with gratitude and thanksgiving at the conclusion of my long march with my precious burden; and I left it with gratitude and thanksgiving at the beginning of my voyage across seas to my Prince. But betwixt that end and that beginning was much anxiety; and I hope I may visit Lyme one day when my mind is at rest, and I can walk abroad on the Cobb without glancing over my shoulder for fear of redcoats after me.

All did not work out as planned at Lyme, for when we had waited two days, my uncle Barlow had word that the master of the ship would not take us, for he was afeared to be discovered and imprisoned should he take Royalist fugitives across seas. So we left Lyme on the second night, taking our boxes with us in a cart, and made for Poole, I still as a boy, and my uncle's attendant; but whiles we were on our way, and trudging wearily uphill beside the cart, came one riding to say the master would take us after all, for his wife had told him, and made it very plain too, that, would he not serve the King in his hour of need, then she would not serve the master when his need came on him; and as, like all honest men, he feared his wife more than he feared the law (and got more satisfaction out of her, too, no doubt), he allowed he would take us.

So back we went and into a small boat on Charmouth beach; whence we were obligated to clamber up a rope ladder the like of which I had never climbed in my life before, and thought every moment to fall off and sink to the bottom with the weight of the belt. (For my uncle Barlow had decided I must wear the belt until we were safe in France, and be a boy till then, too.) But I remembered I was a boy and held on tight and so tumbled over the side on to the deck; and with a fair wind we stood out for France and freedom.

The captain was a fearful man, and would not allow that we were free of arrest until we were fairly into the Seine; but I had no worry on that score, for as soon as the ship began to heave, why, I began to heave with it, and all the way across I cared not whether it was as boy or girl I died, or whether as a free woman or as a Parliament prisoner, so long as the ship sank quickly and sucked me down with it.

But the ship made port in the end, and it was as a stout yet mighty green-faced boy that I stepped on to the shore of France, and staggered into the first French house that ever I was in. 'Twas indeed the house of Master Sambourne, the English merchant that handled the Royalist correspondence. It was the same who stood surety for the King and my lord Wilmot when they returned to France after Worcester fight, and were like to be arrested for penniless vagrants until they found someone to vouch for them.

Master Sambourne stared when my uncle Barlow said that the dirty little boy must have a room to himself and water to wash, for so all mucked over was I that those that saw me doubted that water had ever touched my face before; but he stared still more when I presented myself for supper as a short-haired lady with a pink face and pink hands (albeit the finger-nails were torn), and clad in London fashion.

My uncle Barlow suggested I should change my name again, and would I call myself Mistress Walter or Mistress Protheroe? To which I answered that so long as I was Mistress Walter my father might claim me, or might make mischief for those who had helped me to cross seas; and as for Mistress Protheroe, that was not my name neither. But since my uncle Barlow was to be my guardian in France and to have me under his protection (for such he had promised), I thought the most convenient name for me would be Mistress Barlow, would he be so kind as to allow it.

My uncle Barlow could raise no objection; and master Sambourne agreed that, sure, 'twas the best name I could have chosen, for were master Barlow to parade with a most personable young virgin, tongues would wag unless 'twas known she was his kinswoman.

So Mistress Barlow I became, and Mistress Barlow I have remained, though once I had hoped to change to another name more grand, and one to which, in truth, I have more right. My uncle Barlow was indeed kind to me, and I am ever grateful to him; but he had troubles of his own, and presently he returned to Wales; and, as I have to tell, I did not need his protection for long.

For we took the belt to Paris and my uncle presented it to the Prince (for such was the King's command). Exactly what it contained I never knew; but it is certain the Prince was more in funds after my arrival, if the stories of poverty I heard were true. And as soon as my hair grew again and I was willing to be seen in public, I was presented to the Queen and she was most affable to me. So no doubt I did the Court some service.

And that (said Mistress Barlow) is the true story of how I turned into a boy and carried the King's treasure on my body to France, where I became a woman again. And to what purpose I became a woman I shall tell next. It is the true story of my journey to France, as I hope to be saved.

III France: Ecstasy   (Spring 1648)

I TOLD YOU (said Mistress Barlow) that I was not presented to
Queen Marie [Henrietta Maria] until my hair grew again; but
I could not hide myself from the Prince for so long. For I had
not been in Paris two days before word came to me that the
Prince desired my attendance. And when I sent back word that
my hair was all cut off and ragged and in consequence I was
not fit to be seen, he replied that he did not care what the devil
my hair looked like, it was me he wanted to see, and he was
minded to come and burn the house down and smoke me out
if I did not come to him. And I sent back word that if his
Royal Highness commanded me to come as a loyal subject of
His Majesty, his father, then would I come dutifully. His answer
to that was that he did not as Prince of Wales command me to
come as a Welsh subject of his father's, but that as a man and
a soldier he very mightily desired to converse with me as a brave
and valiant woman; and he sent me a costly scarf to tie round
my head, and a pearl necklace too.

So I went to him the next day, and was ushered into a small
room where he stood alone by the window, drumming on the
sill with his fingers, impatient. He turned round as Mistress
Lucy Barlow was announced, and took a step towards me, boyishly eager, and then he remembered his royal dignity as I
curtsied, and he halted and held out his hand.

But when I had kissed his hand, he pulled me up and held

me by the shoulders and looked me in the face, and I thought
he would kiss me, but he did not then, but he gave me permission to be seated so that we could converse at ease, and so
we sat side by side and chattered for an hour or more, not like
Prince and subject, but like lad and maid.

And mighty pleasant it was to meet him again and to find
that he remembered me and had thought of me during the long
and unhappy years we had been parted, when he had so many
other and more important matters to occupy his attention.

As soon as I saw him, I perceived he had grown taller, and
filled out to be a fine figure of a man, being now eighteen years
old. His black curls fell thickly to his shoulders, but his skin
seemed swarthier than I remembered it was in the moonlight
at Golden Grove, and his hair blacker and his eyebrows thicker;
and the sad lines about his mouth were beginning to take shape.
But he did not look sad whiles I prattled to him, but was very
merry.

'Twas I who gave him the name of the Black Boy, not at
once, but later on, when I knew him better, though I thought
of him as my Black Boy from the day he first kissed me in Wales;
but the nickname took, it was so apt, and for many years now,
where loyal men have gathered together, they have toasted the
Black Boy, and may he come into his own!

He was bolder and more self-assured than when I first saw
him, more like the King he now is; but he was still shy with
me, and I do not think he had ever known a woman, though
he was a Prince with much temptation in his path.

The first thing he said to me when I was alone with him was
that I was handsomer than ever; and he said it again when we
had sat down, and then added that, Faith! he had not thought
it possible. But I said that 'twas impossible I should be handsome without my curls to frame my face.

I still kept the scarf over my head, but he made me take it
off so that he could see what I looked like as a boy—I would
do anything for him, and he guessed as much, though I blushed
for him to see me shorn—and he looked serious at first, from

respect for my lost glory, but then he laughed and said 'twas impossible to believe anyone could have thought I was a boy, for my pretty face gave the lie to my short hair.

And when I asked him, pertly, no doubt (but he liked me so, then) if he meant that my face was a lying face, he said that if I meant it to be taken for a rude boy's, it was, but he had been told that all women's faces were lying faces, though he did not know it of his own experience, yet he'd be damned if Mistress Lucy Walter's face was not as honest as 'twas pretty. And I said that if 'twas as pretty to him as 'twas honest to him, then it must be the prettiest face among all his subjects. And he allowed that certainly it was. And he liked me being pert and saucy to him, so we were very merry and innocent together.

Then he bade me tell him the story of my adventures, and he marvelled at them, though they were not one half so perilous as his own, later, after Worcester fight, the story of which I have heard him tell often. His own black curls were shorn for disguise then, and he told me that as he sat to have the scissors clip-clipping round his ears, he thought of Mistress Barlow and of how she had sacrificed her crowning glory for his sake and his father's. But that was in the future.

He praised me mightily for my part in the enterprise, and pronounced me a very brave lass, and said he wished there were a thousand men in England as loyal and resolute as I was, for my courage and endurance put the men of England to shame.

He seemed sad then, so I made him laugh by telling him how the Roundhead officer kicked me in the Seat of Honour and sent me sprawling in the ditch, and how I could not get up for the weight of the belt, but half knelt with my backside in breeches stuck up in the air before I struggled upright again. At that he laughed mightily, and enquired if the kick had hurt much, and, waxing very bold, asked if he might see the place to see if it was bruised still, but I would not show it to him, I said, not even did he command me as a subject.

But when I told him how the coachman had struck at me with his whip, he was all sympathy, and he stroked the weal gently with his hand, and assured me it hardly showed at all (but my mirror told me it did), and then he suddenly kissed the place, and then he kissed me on the lips, and presently I was in his arms, and we were kissing loverwise.

And we were lovers, too, so far as kisses and sighs and wishes went, from that time forth. There was nothing I would deny him, but he would not take what he could not take with honour. For in those days he was nice about matters of honour, and he respected me as a lady who had suffered for the royal family and done it service.

And in particular I had done a service to him, for which he had been grateful even had I been a dirty little boy; and that was, that I had brought him money. For the King his father had ordered that half the treasure was to go to the Prince and half to the Queen; and before that all the money there was at the Court was held by the Queen, and she kept him plaguey short, and he had to beg guineas from her Lord Germaine [Henry Jermyn, later Earl of St Albans, Chamberlain to Henrietta Maria] for all of his necessary expenses, which was a miserable position for a royal Prince to be in; and sometimes she would refuse him, for she would not realise that her son was a grown man, or perhaps she did not wish to resign her parenthood and accord him his rights. So he was grateful to me because I had brought him the treasure; but 'twas not for that he kissed and cosseted me and was for ever having me in his company and sending me messages and presents. That was for love.

The Prince came to see me, or I went to see him, almost every day, and we were mighty happy together. He never tired of making me tell again the story of my adventures; and sometimes, when he was visiting me, I would put on my boy's garb, so that he could see what I looked like as a boy. But I did not tie my bosom up, nor had I the belt, nor the dirty face, so I was not much like; and he marvelled that anyone could have been so stupid as to mistake me for a loutish boy, and he said that had he known that the plot was that I should tramp across England in this ridiculous and penetrable disguise, why, he would have forbid it, for 'twas unconscionable that anyone could think the business could succeed.

So I screwed up my face and poked out my tongue at him, and spoke in a harsh voice, and he laughed mightily and said that, Faith! I was an actor, and if boys could take the part of lovesick women on the stage, why, a girl such as I could take the part of a saucy knave of a boy. It was not of my seeking that I preserved those rough, dirty garments, and put them on sometimes, but only to amuse the Prince, for I would do anything for him, and if it pleased him to laugh at my appearance, I was resolved he should not want for a laugh.

And so two happy months slid into memory. It was not then that I became his mistris, you must know, though 'twas not for want of desire on his part or mine; but only the scruples that he had, not to deprive me of my honour.

He often said that he would fain marry me and make me his wife before all the world, for he loved me well and truly and he would never love another lass as he loved me; and I believe he spoke truth then. I am sure he has not loved anyone as he loved me, nor ever will again; for I was the first, and he took me in the springtime of his manhood, when to love and be loved was to walk in fairyland.

He told me that he had loved me from the moment he saw me in the moonlight at Golden Grove; and because of me he had kept himself free of women and all the temptations Princes are subject to. But now he honoured and respected me so, he would not dishonour me. 'Twas deadlock. For as a royal Prince he could not marry where he chose; he could dispose his heart where he must, but his hand was not his own. It was his duty to make a rich and powerful alliance so that he could raise an army and drive out the villains who had dethroned his father and were even now oppressing the people of his kingdoms; and we both appreciated that he must do his duty; yet his heart failed him (he told me) when the Queen his mother set him to woo his big-nosed cousin, the Duchess Montpensier, 'La Grande Mademoiselle' as they called her; he tried, but he could not.

He could not endure her (he confessed to me) with her super-cilious airs and her haughty manner, though she was his mother's brother's daughter and the wealthiest heiress in the world. She carried herself, he said, as if she thought the sole purpose of God's Creation had been to culminate in her, and that when Death gave her his icy kiss mankind would come to an end, for God had created perfection in her, and 'twould be purpose-less to continue.

His wooing of Mademoiselle was before I came to Paris, if it can be called wooing when the man is all reluctance and the woman all disdain. So strong was the memory of me in him that he was afeared he might be married off to Mademoiselle before ever he saw me again; so, though he obeyed his mother and wore the lady's colours, and sat at her feet at the play, and handed her into her coach, yet he contrived to impress her with his uncouth and schoolboyish manner, so that Mademoiselle, who was five or six years older than he was, could not contem-plate surrendering her blue eyes and her yellow hair and the tiny soft hands and feet she is so vain of, to this black clod-hopper. So he was saved for me; and often we laughed as he told me of how he had acted the tongue-tied lout in order to keep her ardour within bounds—if indeed, she felt any ardour for him.

I do not know how the Prince and I would have resolved our problem had not Affairs of State rained suddenly on our Spring-time of Love. For he came to me one day with a long face, yet with sparkling eyes, too, and he told me that he was called to fight for his father's kingdom again. Sad he was to leave me, he said, but eager to strike another blow for the crown and the cause of liberty and law.

What had happened was, that the fleet had turned against the Parliament, and had sailed for Holland to put themselves under his charge. The King was a prisoner at Carisbrooke, and they looked to the Prince of Wales to lead them.

There was no love lost between the army and the fleet, for the fleet had been built up by the King's wise ship-money tax which the rich men in Parliament refused to pay, and so they

raised the army to beat the King for putting on the tax. So now
the fleet had declared for the King, and the Prince was to go to
Holland with Prince Rupert, to command them and blockade
the trading ships; so that without the trade on which the English
merchants depended, Parliament would be brought to its senses
and the King would be restored.

My Prince was boyishly eager at the prospect of fighting, and
his one regret was that he could not take me with him; nor
could he tell when we should meet again; nor indeed, for such
are the fortunes and misfortunes of war, whether he would
survive the bloody conflict that he anticipated must ensue. And
he looked forward to landing in England and battles there again,
so that it might be a year or more before he had time for love.

I said that for his sake and to be beside him always and to
share his dangers, I would have my hair shorn again and put on
boy's clothes again, and go with him and be his cabin-boy. But
he was not forward for that. He would not have me risk the
perils and hardships of the sea. I had come unharmed through
England with the two stout fellows to protect me; but to be a
cabin-boy and mix with rough sailors on a man-of-war would
be a great dishonour to me, even if no man did me a mischief.
For he would not be able to have me with him all the time. The
Admiral of a fleet did not spend his time sitting on his backside
giving orders and drinking wine; his was an active life, on deck
in all weathers, going from ship to ship in a cockleshell of a
rowing boat and clambering up overside on ropes, and dining on
salt pork and biscuit; and besides, what use would a cabin-boy
be to him who was lying sick in his hammock all the voyage?
Though I pleaded with him and told him all he said was nonsense, he would not have it.

The Admiral, he said, must have his mind easy, and his
thoughts concentrated on the battle; he must not be distracted
by wondering whether his cabin-boy was spewing his heart out
as the ship rocked, or pouring out his life's blood from a cannon
ball in the guts. It was his duty to be an Admiral, and mine to
sit safe and secure and wait for him to return victorious. For

'twas not as a cabin-boy he desired me, but as a wife; and were it not for his duty to his father to marry a rich woman, he would marry me before he departed to the fleet.

But the more we talked of that, the more we perceived that 'twas impossible. The both of us shed tears at the thought of parting, and of foregoing, perhaps for ever, that blissful union we both desired; and the upshot of it was, that I said, could we be married private and tell no one; and then, when he had reconquered England and his father was King in Whitehall again, he would not need to marry a rich wife, and we could be married again proper. He thought over that, and then he said that, were he killed in the battle, I could announce that I was his wife, and if perchance our marriage had produced a son, the son could be married to Mademoiselle before he was old enough to realise what was happening to him. Which I said was cruel to the little mite; and besides, Mademoiselle would be forty before any son of ours was old enough to marry her, and married herself long since. But he thought no one would marry her ere she was forty, except she were married to a babe in arms who could not protest.

But the next day he came and said that if I were willing for him to engage a chaplain to read the marriage service over us, in a church, solemnly, with no responses by the parties, and no ring, and no written paper, nor witnesses neither, so that we should be married in the sight of Almighty God, though not in the sight of the law; then we could be man and wife so.

I allowed that 'twas the best we could have in the circumstances. And that was the truth of the matter. If it was blasphemous to have our union blessed so, then I am truly penitent. But I had to let him have me, or the both of us would have expired for love.

So, that night, as 'twas gathering dusk, he came in a coach to my lodging, and I went to him alone, and we rode together in the coach, the two of us and the chaplain, who was a grave and silent man I had never seen before, nor since.

And after an hour, or maybe two (for I made no account of

time), when 'twas quite dark, but still warm, for 'twas June, we halted at a little church, solitary by the roadside. I do not know where the church was, nor in what direction from Paris, and I did not care neither, so that it was a church and my Prince was with me.

So we stood side by side before the altar in that silent chancel, where the moonlight made ghostly paths across the floor—Charles Stuart, Prince of Wales, and Lucy Walter, the little Welsh girl, the two of us.

For I paid no account to the chaplain, and the two coachmen holding the candles, nor to the old Frenchman in the shadows, who unlocked the door and let us in, and who mumbled echoes of the chaplain's holy words. They were necessary parts of the furniture, but to me they were not living folk—only the Prince and I were real.

The chaplain read the English marriage service over us. He was a serious and dignified man, and he did not open his lips all the time he was with us, save only to read the service and to say what falls to the minister to say.

So reverent and sincere does he play his part that I cannot but feel I am being married in every particular; and what makes it more real is, that though the Prince has stipulated there shall be no responses and no ring, yet when the time comes for the bridegroom to answer to his name and to vow to take the woman for his wedded wife, he answers manfully, and so I answer in my turn; and when it comes to the putting on of the ring, my Prince plucks from my finger the ring which he had given me at Golden Grove, and passes it to the chaplain, who hands it back to him, and he puts it on my marriage finger. (And here on my finger it is still, for proof that I was married to the King.)

And so, when we come to the ceremony's climax, the Prince looks hard at the chaplain, and the chaplain hesitates a moment, and then he gravely pronounces us man and wife.

And so we were married—Charles Stuart and Lucy Barlow; for indeed I believed that 'twas so, for so confused was I by the giving out of names and the putting on of the ring which I had not expected, that I verily believed that the Prince had planned this surprise for me, that we should be truly married, and this I believed.

And we knelt down then and prayed before the altar. I do not know if the Prince prayed, nor what he prayed for, but I know I prayed with a full heart that there should be a blessing on our marriage, and that I should be a good and a true wife to my husband, and a helpmate to him, and that I should love him always, as indeed I have. So if there has been no blessing from Heaven on our marriage, 'twas not because there was no reverence nor piety in my heart. For I was truly reverent; and penitent, too, for any sin I was about to commit, for I did all I could to make our marriage a true and Christian marriage.

But I was distressed a little that 'twas in a Catholic church we had the ceremony, for I was brought up in the true faith of the Anglican Church, and I should have preferred to be married in it, as I hope to die in it; and so would the Prince, for 'tis his duty as King to protect and support the Protestant Church of England.

However, 'twas the English marriage service that was read over us; yet there was one sin I committed (if sin it be), and that was that, when we knelt to pray after we was made man and wife, I perceived a statue of the Virgin Mary, and I prayed to the Virgin Mary and asked her to bless me and my marriage; and as I knelt there I felt so proud and purified and joyful that I thought I heard her voice accepting my prayer and promising she would bless my marriage. But now I know that 'twas a great sin in me to pray to the Virgin Mary, and to ask her blessing, for my marriage was not lawful, and so it has not been happy —though for the first two years it was, and then all has been misery and despair.

Another thing I did wrong, I think, was to give my name as Lucy Barlow, for that was not my baptised name, and I was not confirmed in it, neither; but the Prince laughed when I confessed my fears of this, and said that 'twas no sin for a wench to change her name, and, whatever the custom was in Wales, why, in Scotland a woman could call herself by whatever name she pleased, and as Scotland was one of his father's kingdoms, he would anticipate his coming to the throne of Scotland and give me his royal dispensation to call myself Mistress Barlow whenever I choose.

Then he added that the dearest wish of his heart was that I should be known before all men as Lucy Stuart, Queen of Scotland. But I said I had no concern with Scotland, but only with his Principality of Wales, to which he replied that the other dearest wish of his heart was that he could marry me so that I would be Princess of Wales, and we could make a Prince of Wales between us.

And in my heart, he said, you are the true and only Princess of Wales.

I had no document to prove the marriage, and there was nought to show 'twas not all a dream of a young virgin's romantic mind—except that there was a certain consequence nine months later, which is living evidence of something, though not necessary of lawful marriage. So, whether 'twas lawful or not, the Prince was free to repudiate the same, which he has often done private, and will no doubt do public should it suit him for reasons of State. But that was how I wished it, for he could not have had me, else, nor I him; and though 'twas a sin and I have had to bear the charge for it, I was full of joy and thankfulness at that time.

So we came out of the church into the moonlight, my husband and I; and I noticed that there were trees around, and owls in them, hooting; and there was the coach waiting with the white road fading into the distance. 'Twas a fairy coach and we drove into fairyland. We sat in the coach, with my head on his shoulder, and his arm around me, and holding hands, and we jolted along, joyful and yet impatient to reach the journey's end. This was a low house set back in the woods, where there was only an old Frenchwoman to wait on us; and there we supped, not very greedily, I am sure, for we were hungry only for love.

And after we had supped, we were shown upstairs to a large

room, sparsely furnished, yet with a competent bed, which was all we desired. My husband pronounced it the competentest bed he ever saw, and indeed I was fain to agree with him. For when he saw the bed, he said that were he to come, in the fullness of time and by God's will, into all the kingdoms of England and Wales, Scotland, Ireland, yes, and France, too—yet there was no kingdom he desired more than that same bed.

And I (complying with his mood, for indeed he could play upon my emotions as upon an instrument) answered him and said that in all his kingdoms, when he came into them as he would, he would not find one subject more loyal, and more eager to serve his pleasure than the subject who now stood before him, which the same I was ready to prove.

So we were alone together, with the bolts shot on the inside, and no servants to rattle the door, nor sentries to stamp their feet outside, nor watchmen to cry the hours. But only the wind in the trees, and the owls calling. We were bedded without ceremony, without witnesses, without friends, without weeping mothers and bawdy, jocular uncles, without the cutting of garters and the flinging of the stocking—but we cared for none of those fripperies. We were eager for each other, and to have each other was all we desired in the world.

Indeed, to have him and for him to have me, is all that I have ever desired in the world, and if I am a sinful woman to confess it, then I confess it, and there's an end to't.

'Twas a true marriage, if love makes a true marriage, though I know it does not; for lawful marriage has nought to do with love, but is a matter of lands that march together, or of jingling guineas in one hand and a resplendent title in t'other, and though the parties to it may look to find a kind of love when they are bedded, why, in bed is the last place where love can be found.

For love that is born in bed and maintained only between the sheets is a sickly child and cannot be reared, and dies as soon as passion dies, and that is rare to survive curiosity, which is its twin. For what love is, is not the desire of the flesh, though that is part of love, and 'tis not the music of a voice, nor the shape of a face, nor the carriage of a body, nor the curve of a limb, though these are a part of love, too, and 'tis not the sheer joy of being with a person, though that is a part of love, nor 'tis honour and respect and trust (for love can subsist where these have been murdered, though but hardly), nor 'tis even the desire to possess and to surrender both at once, nor 'tis understanding and sympathy, though this is important, nor 'tis the imperative necessity to serve and assist and comfort and encourage the person (though this is the heart of love)—for love is the urge to service, and if you do not eagerly and whole-heartedly desire to serve and please and satisfy a man above all other things on earth, why, you do not love him truly; for love is not the willingness to die for a man (for 'tis preferable to live for him); but 'tis all these and more besides, and, most important of all, 'tis the sure conviction that you could not live if the person you love were to die. For if you love truly, you love for ever, and you are shackled to the man, whether he is near or far, and you cannot unlove him, however he may abuse you or fail you; and if he dies, why, you die too, though your body may continue to drag itself over the earth for a dreary while.

All this I know now, for I know what love is, but I did not know it then, and when I disrobed for my marriage bed, I was obsessed with carnal desire and had mind for nought else.

And the Prince was as eager to shed his virginity as I was to surrender mine; and sure lawfully wedded couples never enjoyed more ardent nor more satisfying a wedding night. When I think of all that has happened since, and of all the misery I have endured in consequence of that event, I believe I would endure it all again ten times over to have but once again the joy of that marriage bed.

The longest and sweetest nights come to a dawn at last, and this was a June night, and short, though 'twas the sweetest I have ever spent, or shall spend this side of Heaven. And soon the sun was streaming through the open casement, and birds were singing in the eaves, and a cock crew somewhere, and 'twas a new day, and the opening of my new life, and I awoke to find my Prince sleeping by my side, with his black curls spread on the pillow, and I thought he was truly mine. But now I know that I was truly his, but he was not mine.

We broke our fast then, and the coach carried us back to Paris; but though the morning was bright and I was so happy, yet I fell asleep in my true love's arms. 'Twas little sleep I had had the night before; and 'twas not until we were jolting over the cobblestones of Paris that I woke up properly to think for where I was.

So I do not know which way we came into the city, nor where the church, or the house, was. And once, when I asked the Prince for the name of the place, that I might re-visit it, he said that, Faith! 'twas so outlandish French he could not put his tongue to it, and indeed it had slipped his memory. So I thought he did not intend me to know, and I did not press for it.

And that (said Mistress Barlow) is the true story of how I surrendered my maidenhead and my honour to the Prince of Wales, upon pretence of a true marriage in a church. It is the true story, as I hope to be saved. If I sinned, I repent that I sinned; but it was a marriage of true love, and had I my life over again, I had married the same way again.

And yet the price I have paid has been very high, and unless a maiden loves as deeply and as sincerely as I loved the Prince, the price is not worth the pleasure. No maiden reading my story can fully understand the bliss I had, which was so short; but all can understand the misery that is to follow, and if my story should warn other maidens from surrendering to the lust of men, then perhaps my sufferings have not been in vain.

IV Holland: Illusion   (June 1648-April 1649)

WE HAD THE one night for the consummation of our love (said Mistress Barlow), and then the Prince must needs busy himself with preparations to take command of the fleet. And 'twas a shameful thing that, even when possessed of this occasion to rescue the King his father and recover his kingdom, the Prince had to beg from door to door for the wherewithal to furnish his ships.

One thing we settled was, that he would take me with him to Holland, for English bottoms might not enter the harbours of France, and I would be nearer to him in Holland, where I could be under the care of his sister Marie, the Princess Royal, and her husband, the Prince of Orange. Princess Marie was but a year younger than I, and had been my childhood playmate on occasion. But I had not seen her since she went for Holland to be married in the year forty-one.

I was presented to the Queen, though my hair had hardly grown proper, and she received me graciously, not only because I had brought the treasure from the Tower for her, but because she was very willing that one so brave and loyal (as she said) should go with her son to be his mistris (for so she thought I was), for she considered it but expedient that a lusty young Prince of eighteen should have a mistris, and oft-times she had told him so, but he had not been forward for it because he loved me and, could he not have me, would have no one.

Indeed, in the first transports of his joy at my eager surrender, he confided that, before I came to Paris, he had been minded to end his days as a monk if he could not have me. 'Twas not a resolution that recurred to him when he had had his fill of Mistress Lucy Barlow.

It was June of the year forty-eight, when the Prince took the road for the Low Countries and the ocean. 'Twas a gay and hopeful party he led, for we were all cheerful to think that the King was to be rescued and the Roundheads laid low. We knew not that our hopes were liars, and that ten years would pass and bloody-hearted Cromwell be still sternly in power, and the English ground down under the army.

I passed on that journey for the Prince's mistris, and though 'twas shameful to me, who am a well-brought-up young lady with the royal blood legitimate in her veins, to be accounted as a concubine, yet there was delight in it, too (I must confess), for wherever we lodged o' nights, the Prince and I lay in the best room and private, and he forgot the cares of State and the coming battles in the comfort of my arms.

And everyone treated me with deference, too—save one young fellow, some squire whose name I knew not, who uttered some slighting jest, which, when the Prince heard of it, he knocked him down, and bade him begone, saying he would have none about him who was not properly respectful to Mistress Barlow. So the fellow slunk off, and I never saw him again, but I doubt not he is one of those who have spread lies about me.

'Twould have been a happy journey had I not been afeared my Prince might be killed in the fighting to come. The loyal fleet lay at Helvoetsluys, so the Prince and Prince Rupert made for Calais and sailed thither in an English frigate; and on that short voyage I was not sick. But the Prince would not suffer me to sail further with him, but sent me to The Hague, where the Princess Marie and her husband received me very graciously and found me a decent lodging, and would have entertained me at their Court, only I fell ill with anxiety for the fate of the Prince, and perhaps, too, with the first stirrings of the young

Prince I was to bear my Master in the coming springtime. So I kept close in my lodgings, in ordinary, and my husband visited me there in the hours he could snatch from fitting out the fleet.

The Duke of York was at The Hague, and a fine fit of sulks he was in, too. He was not yet fifteen, but he had thought the command of the fleet should be given to him, for he had the title of Lord High Admiral, but 'twas an empty title since he wanted years and knowledge to command a fleet; and he was envious that the Queen had said flat that 'twas the elder brother's right to command the King's forces whiles the King was in captivity. And Charles was resolved on it, too; which was the beginning of the dissension between the brothers. There were sharp words between 'em over the business, and the Prince told me that the Duke was not only disgruntled, but was gruntled to boot. And, indeed, I never saw a more gruntled boy than the Duke of York when his brother would not allow him to command the ships. But 'twas my undoing in the end; for 'twas not only the fleet he envied his brother for, but his mistris also.

The Duke was a long-faced, sour-looking boy even then, as he is now a long-faced, sour-looking man; and I liked not the way he stared at me. I thought, from his ogling me when I was presented to the Princess, his sister, that he would as lief have his brother's wife as his brother's ships. And I resolved to put the nasty boy in his place, so when he said with a simper that he wondered that I could have passed for a boy, I retorted that I did not wonder at all that he had been able to escape from England in petticoats disguised as a girl. 'Twas injudicious of me to make an enemy of him, but he angered me by his ogles and his glances. Had I been wiser, I had kept a shut mouth; but my mouth is a Welsh one, and won't keep shut under insult. So my sharp tongue was my undoing. For, later, when Charles wished to make peace with his brother for the sake of recovering his throne, he allowed the Duke to poison his mind against me, and to tell him lies about me. But the Duke did not have his way with me, neither.

The Prince's adventure with the fleet did not prosper, for the
tarry-breeks were a contentious lot, and he could not bring them
to battle order but once, and then the wind failed and the Parliament ships escaped; and some of the Prince's ships broke away,
and sailed back to the mercies of Cromwell, and t'others spent
their time in disputing amongst themselves, so that there was
no sense in 'em. And the food ran short. So in the autumn the
Prince came on shore and left Prince Rupert in command of all
that were left.

My husband was struck with the small-pox then, and nearly
died of it, and I wished to nurse him, for I cared not whether
I lived or died if he died, but he would not suffer me to come
nigh him, because of my condition, and, praise be God! he
recovered, and his face was not marked, neither; and I did not
catch the small-pox, though I was all but dead with anxiety and
grief for him.

Yet I have often thought since that 'twould have been merciful
of God to have taken me to Him then; for the greater part of
the happiness of my life was over by that Christmas of the year
forty-eight, though I did not know it then. If 'tis a sin to wish
to die, then I have sinned grievously, for oft-times I have wished
I had died at The Hague that winter. Had I died then, I should
have wanted many happy days and happenings for which I am
thankful, and in particular my two children, which are the living
proofs of my love for the King, and many happy hours in his
company and his service; but I should not have had to endure
the knowledge of his perfidy and unfaithfulness. But God was
not cruel in allowing me to live, and it has been wicked of me
to wish to escape the punishment for my sin.

That Christmas of forty-eight was not a gay one, in truth,
for over it hung the rolling thunder-cloud of the fate of the
imprisoned King. Though 'twas not till January he was brought
to his mock trial, and not till the end of January that the man
of blood, brute Cromwell, had his wicked way; yet 'twas known
to us at The Hague that the Roundhead army was clamouring
for the trial, and would have nothing but the trial; and the

outcome filled us all with dread. So there was little merry-making
at The Hague that Christmas.

The Prince, indeed, had hardly any other thought but to save
his father's life; but there was little he could do. He writ his
name at the foot of a blank sheet of paper and sent it to Fairfax
by a trusted messenger, saying the Parliament could write on
it what they willed, even to his own imprisonment and life, so
they would spare the King's life, and he would abide by it. But
the Roundheads would have nothing but the sacred blood of
the King, and I do not know what became of the Prince's paper.
He sent another such sheet to his father, which was but a gesture
to show that he loved him, and would give his life for him; but
the King loved his son equally, and he put the paper in the
fire; and whether father was nobler than son in this, or t'other
way round, I cannot tell, but the Prince demonstrated that he
was all that a Prince should be. But he could not save his father's
life.

'Twas a family party that the Princess Royal and her husband
of Orange gathered round them—the Princess's brothers, and the
Prince's sisters, and their mother; and my husband's aunt, the
Queen of Bohemia [Charles I's sister, Elizabeth], and her sons
Rupert and Maurice and ten or a dozen of their sisters—I always
lost count of these Palatine princesses, and I never could tell
t'other from which. At The Hague also was the Duke of Buckingham [George Villiers the second, 1628-87], and he was a
mad fellow in those days, as he is still.

I was uneasy to venture among all these princes and princesses,
for although most of 'em had no countries and existed on charity,
and although my own grandmother was cousin to Queen Elizabeth [of England], and though I was the wife of the chiefest
prince among 'em (for so I thought myself), yet they none of
them knew I was his wife, and they all deemed me his mistris,
and though 'twas an honour to be the mistris of the Prince of
Wales, and his only true love, yet 'twas not as a concubine that
I wished to appear at Court, but as the wife of the Heir Apparent
and the Queen to be. And shy I was, too, because I was getting

a big belly, and a maid whose belly swells for the first time is ashamed, even if she is an acknowledged lawful wife, which I was not.

So though I made one of the party at times, and they all treated me very civilly—except the Duke of York, who ogled me as if he hoped that the next time I should be childing it should be by him—yet at times, too, I pleaded that I was indisposed and kept my room. The Princess Marie was in particular most solicitous, and satisfied herself that I wanted for nothing necessary for my condition.

I said just now that I could never tell the Palatine Princesses apart, but one I could, and that was Sophia, for my husband was partial to her—or she to him, rather—and oft-times he walked on the Voorhout with her, so that malicious tongues carried it to me that she had a mind to marry him and be Queen of England like her grandmother [Anne of Denmark, wife of James I], which I knew was impossible, since I was his wife, but I did not let that out. And ones who desired to be kind to me, thinking I was afeared that this Princess would put my nose out of joint, reported that 'twas he who would marry her, but she would not have him, for she did not believe he would ever be King, but always a beggar prince, like her father, who had been King of Bohemia for one short winter and was Count Palatine first, though he had been driven out of his lands and died ere he could see 'em again. But I had no envy of the poor wretch, for she was ill-favoured, and my husband confided to me that he gave nought for her looks, nor for her conversation neither, but walked with her for civility's sake, and because he pitied her plainness and her lack of wit, and would more gladly have walked on the Voorhout with me but that my condition prevented it.

Nor would the Prince suffer me to walk anywhere that snowy and slippery winter, for he said that whereas last year I had carried the King's Treasure outside of my belly, now I carried a King's Treasure within, and must be even more careful to preserve one than t'other.

AW   E

When he sat with me, the Prince was in high spirits, and so was I for his sake. Indeed, he was mighty proud of my big belly, which was more than I was. Yet I suppose 'tis a cause of satisfaction to a growing lad to have visible proof that he is a man, and has the capacity to get a maid with child. And with princes, 'tis even more so. He cherished high hopes that in the spring he would be father of an heir, and he swore to me that when I was delivered of my burden, he would marry me before all the world if his father, the King, would give his consent; and then my son—for he swore 'twas a man-child I carried, it kicked so—would be King one day in his turn—a King with English, Welsh, Scots, French, Italian and Danish blood to rule over the three kingdoms.

He added that 'twas a pity Ireland was left out, but the Irish were a savage lot, and would have to be content that the Queen was the beautifulest queen Ireland had ever had.

But I knew his father would not consent, for though I was gentle by birth, and had royal blood in my veins, and was cousin to Queen Elizabeth, as well as the Earls of Essex and Northumberland, and the Earl of Salisbury and the Earl of Suffolk and the Earl of Leicester, yet I was not an heiress; and 'twas obligatory on the Prince of Wales to marry for riches and great alliances and not for love alone.

All the world knows how the poor King, Charles the First, was taken to Westminster Hall to be mocked and abused, and then to Whitehall to be shamefully done to death; and so my husband became King Charles the Second.

Grieved indeed was I to hear of the King's horrid murder, and I wept for sorrow at the sadness of it, with no thought of my own plight and how it would be affected. For I well remember his sad dignity when I served him at Golden Grove, as if his destiny hung over him and he was aware of it. But then I took comfort for myself, for I thought that now my master was King he would marry me, for he needed no man's permission, nor his mother's neither. 'Twas foolish of me to think so, but to tell the truth, I was all muddled up in my mind betwixt

minded to pray to the Virgin Mary that when I was brought
to bed of my child, I might die of it, and the child too. Only
I was afeared to pray so, for 'twas blasphemous.

So all night I was wakeful and crying, and the child stirred
and kicked within me, as if he shared my grief and anxiety,
the which perhaps he did, sensing that he was to be born a
bastard, and protesting at it. And if ever poor betrayed wench
was in despair and misery and wished to die, it was Mistress
Lucy Barlow on that bitter cold February night at The Hague.

But in the morning the King came again, and went down
on his knees to the poor betrayed Welsh girl, and protested
that he was mighty sorry he had been angry with me, that he
had lain awake all night for thinking of me, and he swore that
he loved me and would always love me, and only me, and that
when he came into his own, why, he would marry me in Westminster Abbey, and the Archbishop of Canterbury should pronounce us man and wife, and all the peers and peeresses of
England, Scotland and Ireland should shout, 'Amen! Long live
King Charles and Queen Lucy!'

But 'twas expedient to keep our marriage in the dark for the
present, for did he marry me now, he would never gain his
throne, and I should never be a real queen.

He was so gay and so cheerful and so coaxing and so kind
that I allowed him to dry my eyes and wipe my nose and kiss
my mouth and comfort me; though I did not believe a word of
it. I knew there was no help, and that I must resign myself to
my fate, for though he might come to his throne in the chances
and changes of life, yet he would not marry me then, for there
would be those about him that would prevent him, and he
would be obligated to marry some princess. The most I could
hope for was to retain his love. And as for my high hopes and
ambitions, they were but illusions.

So I smiled at him till I produced the dimples for him to kiss;
and I told him that I knew now that I should never be his
Queen, and could only be his mistris, but that I would rather
be the mistris he loved and lay with for his pleasure than the

Queen he loved not and lay with only in the way of his duty to his country.

But he swore that if he could not marry me, he would not marry anyone; and, in the end, I allowed him to persuade me to pretend I believed him. (And, indeed, he has kept his promise, and has not married anyone, though he has been many times talked of for marriage; but neither has he remained faithful to the vows he made to me before God in that church hidden in the lonely woods outside Paris. But that came later. . . .)

So we kissed and made it up and were friends again, and were to be lovers again, too. But though I allowed him to persuade me that he loved me and intended to do right by me when his occasions permitted, yet I insisted on one thing, and that was that I should not be brought to bed at The Hague, where all his royal cousins were, and all his advisers, too; for Master Hyde [Sir Edward Hyde, later first Earl of Clarendon, then Chancellor of the Exchequer] and other fussy gentlemen had come to surround the new King and keep him away from his loving Welsh mistris; and I was resolved to go hence until I could appear in the company in my natural shape and without shame.

He agreed readily enough to my going away, and I think he was glad rather than sorry at our parting, for all my looks and my figure had left me, and I was in no good spirits neither, so I could neither satisfy him with my body nor amuse him with my raillery. He was a very worried young King and I was no manner of use to him. But I think now I was mistaken in leaving him, for I had taught him the delights of love and he was not willing to forego them whiles I was suffering the consequences; and he looked for other wenches, though I do not know if he found any at that time, for 'twas not till the year following that he planted a bastard on Mistress Betty Killigrew.

So 'twas agreed I should lie in at Rotterdam; and the King asked my cousin Robin Sidney, who had served in the Parliament army but was now an officer in the English Regiment in the Low Countries, and who professed the wish to do the new King some service, to squire me on the journey and to make all arrangements necessary for my comfort and safe delivery.

My cousin Sidney treated me mighty civil, and did all that could be done for a woman in my state and condition. So solicitous was he that the good wife where I was lodged thought he was the father of my child, at which we laughed merrily, for we had not met at The Hague until I was as big as a house, and before that I had not seen him since we were boy and girl in London before the civil strife.

Yet not once nor twice he looked at me with desire in his eyes, and held my hand longer than was needful in handing me from the coach, and I knew that 'twas in his mind to make proposals to me. But he did not, and always treated me honourable. He made himself agreeable, and I liked him well enough, but had he offered to marry me, I would not have had him, for I held myself pledged to the King, and I had lips for no man else. Even had I known the King was to betray me with other women and abandon me at last, I had not married Robin, handsome though he is and polite—not like his rat-faced brother Algernoon, who is a man of plots and earnest dissertations, and one I disliked in childhood and am glad I have not seen since.

So I was brought to bed at Rotterdam, in the month of April, in the springtime of the year forty-nine, many miles from the King my husband, and far distant from my mother, and with no woman friend to comfort and encourage me in my labour.

The man-midwife vowed I screamed and groaned and kicked as though I was bringing forth a dozen twenty-pound striplings, instead of one skinned rabbit weighing half-an-ounce—which was a lie (he was all of seven pounds) and not funny neither. So I told him that he'd better bribe some lusty young fellow to get him with child and engage me to deliver him, and then we'd see who screamed the loudest. But he said that all the brats he was capable of having were by proxy, and I believed his word, since I had no desire to prove the truth on't, for his fangs were

brown and broken, and his breath smelt like Drury Lane on a
hot summer's night.

Even so, he did the business for me, and the results of my
screams and grunts, and his arts and practices (for I suppose he
did something for his fee, though it seemed to me that all that
had to be done, I was doing, and I was too worn and bothered
to see or care what the devil he did), was a boy who was a prince
indeed, plump as butter and full-throated. Sure no finer prince
was ever born, and he would be acknowledged Prince of Wales
by all the world if he had his rights, which perhaps he may
have some day. . . .

And that (said Mistress Barlow) is the story of how I bore
a son to my King and husband, and, if God wills, a Prince of
Wales to my country. That is the true story, as I hope to be
saved.

V Paris: Doubt (May 1649-May 1650)

I HAD THE KING'S son christened James (said Mistress Barlow), which was the name the King chose, for 'twas his grandfather's and the name of the Scots kings for generations; and whoever says he was named for his uncle, the Duke of York, he lies. James is his name, but I always call him Jacky, for his nurses called him Jacques, which is the French form of James.

I loved the boy because he was the son of his father even more than for the pain and suffering he cost me to bring him into the world; and I loved him for himself, too, for even as a babe he was a merry little fellow. And 'twas a great grief to me to have to put him out to nurse. But that I was obliged to do, for the King commanded my attendance at Paris, and 'twas my duty and my desire to obey the King my husband in all things.

So I deposited the mite with a decent woman at Schiedam to nurse, and went to the King. She was a French woman, so that Jacky should learn the French language, as befitted a Prince.

'Twas a poor Court the King held at St Germain, for the guineas I had brought from the Tower had long since melted the way all guineas melt, and the King subsisted on allowances from his cousin of France [Louis XIV], and such sums as could be scraped together by his followers, but only few of 'em had any money. Indeed, the only gentleman about the Court to display any affluence was my Lord Germaine, the Queen's Master of the Horse—or rather, he would have been Master of her Horse had she possessed any horses at that time.

The poverty I could have endured, for poverty was my accustomed lot, and I ever placed love afore luxury; but that was not the most I had to bear, for times had changed, and the King with them. No longer was he the careless young Prince of Wales, domineered over by the Queen his mother, and scarce allowed a sou for spending; but now he was King in his own right, and one who could dispense favours and places (albeit in anticipation only, for the places about him are arduous and worthless until he regains his throne), and who had to occupy himself with schemes and plots to reconquer his kingdoms.

So I found it plaguey hard to come by the King in his new state, for he was surrounded by earnest and voluble advisers, who, though they knew not how they would pay for their next meal (nor their last one, neither), knew well enough what the King must do to drive the Roundheads out and provide sumptuous nourishment for 'em all. Only no two of 'em advised alike, and all were in dissension one with another—and quick on the draw too, so that, had not the King forbad duelling, all his Council had like to have run each other through; so the poor King knew not who to turn to for advice, and was glad enough to forget the cares of State in my apartment, when he was allowed leisure from affairs for the same.

But that was not so frequent as I, or he either, desired. For the one thing all his garrulous advisers were agreed on was that the King must marry a rich heiress, and that his Welsh mistris, being heiress to no estate, was no manner of advantage to him in that enterprise; indeed, they would have the young man continent for his future's sake (and their own futures, too), and they intrigued against me, and invented all manner of business to keep us apart.

His mother the Queen knew well the love between us, and she was gracious to me, for my prattle made her laugh, and laughter was hard to come by in that ragged and contentious Court; but yet she had it represented to me private that she

would not have me prominent there, nor let it be thought that
I was more than a necessary convenience to the King; for she
intended he should make a becoming and politic marriage, and
he must therefore be unencumbered at all convenient times to
dance attendance on Mademoiselle, and to pay court to the same,
and not be for ever in a window-seat dallying and giggling with
me, which he would be whenever he could, since my company
amused him and that of La Grande Mademoiselle and t'other
grand French ladies bored him to silent screams.

I was sore distressed at this tattle of the King's marriage; but
when I demanded of him whether he designed to marry a French
heiress, he laughed and said that, Faith! he did not know where
he would find a French heiress willing to marry a King without
a throne or a crown or an army, or revenue, or an acre of land,
or even a couple of sous to toss to a beggar.

To which I said that even did he find such an heiress, he
would not be happy with her, for 'twas his humour to be easy
and familiar at some times and overbearingly dominating at
others, and with a rich wife he could be neither one nor t'other.
For such a one would not accommodate herself to his mood as
I did, but would expect it to be all t'other way around, and
would belike be haughty and over-proud of her wealth (since
'twas the compensation of God that rich heiresses had nought
but their estates to recommend 'em, and certainly neither the
faces nor the figures to attract a man else), and be for ever flinging
it in his teeth that she had brought him every guinea in his
breeches pocket, whereas he had brought her nought but the
misery and labour of childbed; for such a one would not bear
the fruits of his loins in love and pride as I had done, but only
for duty to continue the royal line.

(Though why anyone should desire to continue a royal line
when every one of 'em, save only his grandfather, King James,
had died by the headsman's axe or the assassin's dagger, or in
the ranks of a defeated army, puzzled me to understand—but
I did not say this to the King, since his father was so lately done
to death by bloody-hearted Cromwell in Whitehall.)

But the King said he did not look for happiness in this world, but was content only to do his duty in it, for had not the preacher said that men were born to trouble as the sparks flew upward? And could he but do his duty by the country and his people, and strike a few sparks out of brute Cromwell's breast-plate, and kick him down to hell where he belonged, why, then he would die happy, even though he lived in wretchedness and contention.

To which I replied that if he was going to quote preachers to me, I would quote at him from the plaguey long and dull sermon he had snored through in the Protestant Church some weeks since, when Dean Cosin was sick and his pulpit was occupied by a long-faced country fellow, but barely breeched, who took as his text Proverbs xv, 17: 'Better a dinner of herbs where love is, than a stalled ox and hatred therewith'. And I did not know why the devil the fool spoke to such a text when those who were obliged to hear him fared for the most part on dry bread and water, and would have esteemed it a feast to sit down to a dish of herbs; so I thought it not irreverent to imitate his voice and his speech in order to amuse the King, so that he laughed till the tears came into his eyes, and he nearly rolled off his chair, and I am sure he will remember that text all his life.

But though he laughed most heartily at my play-acting, he would not heed the sermon, for he said that man was not brought into this world for his happiness, and the proof of it was, that he was born in pain, and as soon as his eyes opened on the world and he realised he was alive in it, why, he let out a great bellow of terror and anticipation; and man was destined to die in agony, too; so why should he expect anything but misery and disappointment meanwhiles? Indeed, he said, he envied often his elder brother [Charles, b. & d. 13 May 1629], who was of greater wisdom than himself, for he took one look at the world and straightaway choked his way out of it. And, as for the wretch who had followed him and had not had the sense to follow him out (by which my husband meant himself), why, the only happiness he knew was when he was with Lucy Barlow, or maybe when he was gallop-

ing a-horseback in the country air, or sailing a boat in a stiff
breeze; for all the rest was boredom or downright disagreeable,
and he only endured it because 'twas in the line of duty.

And when I said, a pox on his duty! he said that 'twas his
resolve to recover his three kingdoms and rule them till he died,
and he would tolerate no let or hindrance in the way of that.
That resolve was paramount and governed all.

When I asked him, did he recognise that 'twas his sacred duty
to throw me over and marry Mademoiselle because I (who loved
him to distraction) was poor, and she (who did not like anything
of him) was rich, he said then, that had he the power to follow
his own inclination, he desired nothing else in the world than
to have me for his wife and constant companion, and, moreover, had we lived in the days before polygamy was made a
crime, why, he would have married me in every cathedral in
Europe, with every Archbishop in turn pronouncing us man and
wife, and then marry but one heiress once for her money and
for nought else and be damned to her; but since that was impossible, then, if it was his duty to his country to marry Mademoiselle and she would consent to have him, why, he would
do it, though he be then obliged to lie with her, the which
he shrank from as a child shrinks from physic; for he understood
but too well that to be a real King he might not minister to
his own tastes, but must undertake many disagreeable tasks
and make the best of 'em with what fortitude he could
muster.

And when I smiled unbelieving, he swore that 'twas true,
that he would as lief wash the feet of fifty dirty beggar-women
as get into bed with Mademoiselle.

The which I said was all damned balderdash, and he knew it,
and I didn't believe a word of it, and particularly the part about
Mademoiselle being as sour as physic, for she was tall and fair,
and neither ugly nor unshapely for a Frenchie, and her breath
did not stink neither, so I doubted not he would do her business
to-morrow and with relish, if she would have him.

He swore that, Faith! that was not true, but he conceded

that, maybe, her person was not so distasteful as he had implied, and that 'twould not be an intolerable penance to have to do with her in bed, though to marry her would be arduous because of her unconscionable conceit of herself.

And when I demanded how he could contemplate marriage with Mademoiselle, or indeed with anyone, seeing that immediate before I was brought to bed of his son he had promised me faithful on his knees that when he had his throne he would marry me in public and make my child legitimate and heir to all his three kingdoms, he replied that, Faith! he loved me so, he would promise me anything if I cried enough for it, but that I could not expect a King to carry out his promises should they conflict with his duty to his country.

To which I said that, as for his duty to his country, he ought to consider his duty to me.

But he only laughed at that, and said he would do it any night I chose to name; and I could not get any more sense out of him, for he kissed and caressed me so that I was obliged to yield all on the instant, and, indeed, I loved him so much he could do aught he wished with me, and so long as I had his love, nought else mattered.

When I had his love, nought else mattered; but for all that, the things I had to endure were hard, and my spirits and my temper suffered for it. For I knew in my heart that I could not rely on his word, and that I should never be his acknowledged wife, but only his mistris. Hope had not deserted me at that time, but reason told me that my hopes were but illusions.

'Twas in Paris then that I learned in the bitter way that what we see in the mirrors of our minds is not what other people see when they look at us. My picture of Lucy Barlow as a pure and innocent young maid who loved the King more than a man had ever been loved before, was but foolish distortion; for what the world saw was just another flaunting harlot. Mine was not read as one of the great love stories of history, but as a target for backhand jeers and sordid jests. She is a wise and sad and disillusioned wench who can see herself truly as the world sees her.

I had been happy enough to be his mistris and to minister to his love could I have kept private, and had I not to meet the down-nose stares of other women at Court. But this is a world in which there is a price for all pleasure, and when the pleasure is sinful, why, the price is double; and the price of my sin was that all the world sneered at me behind my back, and much of it scorned me to my face. No longer was I the brave lass who had brought a lifeline to the sinking ship at the risk of her liberty and her honour, as I had been the year before; nor was I the shy and modest maid who dreamed of marrying the fairyland prince. I was now the bold hussy who was the King's mistris and the mother of his bastard; and though that fact gave me a recognised position at Court, yet 'twas not a position I craved to be recognised in.

For what I was deemed to be I was received wherever I went, according to the natures of those I met. Some were civil enough, and some should have been ashamed to be so cruel to an unfortunate wench. The treatment meted out to me since my shame became public has convinced me that 'tis fear or envy that animates my sex when they contemplate a harlot, and hope or despair the male. For either the women who pointed the finger of scorn at me were no better than they ought to have been themselves and were afeared to be classed with me did they not condemn me, or else they were chaste only because they wanted the occasion to be otherwise. And as for the boastful sex, either they concluded that where one man had succeeded they too could be accepted, or else they were so diffident of their attractions (and with good reason, too) that they realised my favours were out of their reach. So the poor wretch who loses her reputation is despised by the men who believe they can assist her to maintain it in all its blemish, and damned by those who know they can not.

No wench can remain shy and modest when she is aware that wherever she passes she is pointed out for an whore; so I was obliged to assume the airs of a bold hussy perforce, though they became me not and I misliked myself for it. But since I could not nourish my self-respect by claiming to be a lawful wife, I had necessary to stick out my chin and outstare the women of the Court as if to intimate that I knew they were not obliged to line up with me only because they wanted the misfortune of having been found out. And as for the men, I was civil to those who were civil to me, but if a man eyed me or bespoke me as if he took me for an whore, then I let him see I suspected him for a by-blow, the which, for all he or I knew to the contrary, he may well have been.

One of those who was more than ordinary civil to me was Harry Bennet [afterwards Earl of Arlington], but such liking as I had for him was because of his civility to me and not for the man himself; for his manner was pompous, and he uttered long and grand speeches, and for a time I suspected that his object was to have me speak for him for a place. He was indeed employed to perform some secretarial service for the Duke of York, but no doubt he wished for a better. But at length it came out that he was attempting to perform for the Duke what one gentleman would scorn to perform for another, even for a prince, for he sat with me for the space of two hours one afternoon, extolling the virtues of that same Duke, and concluded by asking why I did not look with favour on the King's brother, seeing I looked with favour on the King himself. To which I replied that I looked with particular favour on no man save only the King, for I esteemed myself as much pledged to the King as if I were his lawful wife, and so all other men were indifferent to me, though I owned some were more indifferent than others; and as for the young Duke, I was afeared from the way he ogled me that he had designs on my virtue, and if he had, why, Colonel Bennet could tell his Royal Highness that he had no more hope with me than with his Aunt Eliza—by which I meant not his aunt, the Queen of Bohemia, but only as the saying goes. And I went on to say that Colonel Bennet himself was very welcome to pay his respects to me, in the civil manner he had done hitherto, whenever he pleased (save only when I was engaged with the King), but if all he had to say to me was, that the Duke of York was an estimable young man (which no doubt he was, for all I knew or cared), he might as well save his legs and his breath for his duelling.

Harry Bennet did not visit me so frequent after that, so I supposed he was so filled to bursting with the virtues of the Duke of York that he could not trust himself not to spill over with 'em in my company, and so deemed it safer to stay away.

My Lord Taafe [later first Earl of Carlingford] was another who made himself agreeable to me, but on his own account, and not in behalf of another. For he told me straight out that if there was any little favour he could do me at any time (save only that it concerned the expenditure of money, of which he had none), I had only to send for him and he would drop all and come at once (even were he in the act of pressing his sword-point through his opponent's breast), for he was sure he could give me satisfaction, and gain satisfaction in the doing of it for himself. And so that I could have no doubt as to his meaning, he added that he well knew that the King was a busy man, and unable to carry out all the business for which he was responsible, and that the King had intimated to him (my Lord Taafe) that he was to be employed as deputy or agent to carry out certain matters which the King, owing to lack of time or inclination, could not carry out for himself. (And so my Lord was presently employed, but only in the negotiating of treaties and suchlike.)

I was much enamoured of my Lord Taafe's impudence, and I replied to him gravely that, so far as any business transactions between the King and myself were concerned, the King had hitherto never neglected to find the necessary time to carry 'em out to the infinite satisfaction of both parties, and I did not doubt but 'twas his intention to devote suitable energies to the same in the future, so that for the present I had no need for any assistance of any kind other than pecuniary; but I was much obliged for the compliment implied in my Lord Taafe's kind offer, and would take the liberty of regarding him as a particular friend, and would call upon him should I ever require help of a kind which he had the capacity to perform, a contingency which I was bound to confess seemed to me to be infinitely remote.

To which he replied that I could rest assured that no man had a greater capacity to assist me, for his capacity was well tried and infinite, and his desire to please me was infinite also.

So I told him that my gratitude for his offer was as infinite as his solicitude for my happiness, and I should be infinitely obliged if he would take himself to the devil.

And so we parted good friends. Nor did he scruple, on subsequent occasions when he came to Court (for he was for ever running messages between the King and my Lord Ormond in command of the troops in Ireland), to remind me that his offer still held good—nor I to express surprise and regret that he had so far failed to carry out my injunction.

Had I been in truth what he mistook me for, he had been successful in his attack, for he is an Irish man, and he has a way with him which a maid can barely resist; but I loved the King and was resolved to keep myself pure for him. Indeed, it had been High Treason to surrender to another man what I held in trust for the King.

Oft-times, however, I was obligated to tolerate the company of gentlemen who were impudent without being witty, the which was not so pleasant. One such ill man who regarded me as if I were a dollop of horse-dung which he'd trodden in by inadvertence was a certain Master Evelyn [John Evelyn, F.R.S., 1620-1706], who had the misfortune once—'twas my misfortune, too—to share with me my Lord Wilmot's coach on the drive from Paris to St Germain.

'Twas true that we met not in happy circumstances, for 'twas August, and plaguey hot, and my Lord Wilmot's coach the oldest and cheapest to be had, so that the three of us must sweat and jolt together for twelve miles until we were heartily sick of one another. Nor was the manner of our introduction agreeable to Master Evelyn, for my Lord Wilmot [afterwards first Earl of Rochester, d. 1658], who was most civil to me, had promised

to bring his coach to carry me to pay my respects to the Queen
Mother, and when he arrived at my lodging he had Master
Evelyn with him, and he asked my permission for Master Evelyn
to share the coach, to which I replied that I should be honoured
by the company of any friend of Lord Wilmot's; but Master
Evelyn looked down his pointed nose at me, as if astonished
that my permission should have been requested.

So 'twas not a merry party that trundled to St Germain that
sticky afternoon, though, indeed, I doubt that any party was
merry which included Master Evelyn. He was a man of a long
and misshaped countenance, and a hang-dog air, as if ashamed
of his passions, and defiant of 'em, too; and he would not look
me in the face, neither, but kept glancing at me sideways with
a blush and a simper, by which I could well perceive that he
thought I was easy game, and that he would have had me had
he durst, and yet felt that 'twas shame to him that he should
be stirred by my beauty, and greater shame to me that I should
be aware that he was stirred. For so does your Puritan ever eye a
suspected harlot, and blame her because God has given him both
a man's passions and a coward's heart that durst not indulge 'em.

Master Evelyn said nought to me at first, but addressed all
his remarks to my Lord Wilmot, as if the King's mistris had
neither the wit nor the right to converse with gentlemen; and
when I resolved to show him that I was not to be trodden on,
and insisted on breaking in and demonstrating that even a harlot
has feelings and opinions, he had recourse to the expedient of
explaining whatever he said very simply and carefully, making
me to be a child that wanted both intelligence and elementary
information. But I was not having that, neither, so when there
came an interval in the conversation, I begged him to favour
me with an account of some of the battles and sieges he had
taken part in during the civil strife, for I could see that he was
of a competent age to have borne arms for the King.

To which he replied that he had not fought in the late wars,
and when I enquired of him why not, and was it by reason of
the fact that he suffered from physical disability which was not

outwardly evident, he explained that he had taken horse and sword and servant and joined the King's army in forty-two, but had arrived just after the defeat at Brentford, and the army then retreating to Gloucester and the King having no present use for his services and giving him permission to travel abroad, he had left his horse and his servant with the army and had occupied his next several years visiting famous places in Italy and France and examining their marvels and beauties of buildings and painting.

So I answered that I supposed from what he had said that he was more suited to examine fine paintings and old buildings than to charge alongside Prince Rupert at the Roundheads, since some men were good for one thing and some for another, and in this world, 'twas every man to his trade. To which he replied, aye, and every woman too.

So there we rested with honours easy, and jolted along a mile or two more the while my Lord Wilmot related to us a merry misfortune which befel his cornet at the fight at the ford at Newburn in forty; but as Master Evelyn did not esteem this story worth more than a thin smile, we fell silent.

At length Master Evelyn demanded of me, had I a son, for he had heard tell I had; and where was he, for he had heard tell he was at nurse in Holland; and I replied that, indeed, I had a son, who was the King's son too, as no doubt Master Evelyn was aware; and the King had commanded me to put the boy out to nurse and to attend him in Paris, the which I had done, since 'twas the King's wish, and I was the King's servant and obedient to him in all things.

At which Master Evelyn smiled more broadly than he had done at my Lord Wilmot's merry anecdote, and said that he did not doubt that 'twas the King's wish that I should be with him in Paris, nor did he doubt that I was the King's very good servant, for such was my reputation. And I said that it did not surprise me to be told that such was my reputation, for 'twas true indeed, and I was proud of it; and that, had he and those like him but served the late King in a man's way as I served the present King in a woman's way, perhaps the late King had been alive yet and master of his kingdoms, and the now King wealthy and happy at St James's, instead of a needy exile in Paris; and that, moreover, had Master Evelyn remained with the army instead of leaving his servant to fight in his stead, he too might have earned a reputation I should have heard of.

All he could say to that was that many men had fought and been killed in the civil strife and were forgotten already, but that he conceived that he would be remembered for many generations to come by reason of the fact that he was writing a daily journal or record of everything he saw and did, the which would be of intense interest to our descendants. So I said I hoped he would mention driving with the King's mistris to St Germain, so that I too might be remembered after I was dead; and he said he would. And my Lord Wilmot, winking at me, told him not to neglect to mention that 'twas in his coach, so that he too would be the admiration of posterity for his enterprise in introducing the famous John Evelyn to Mistress Barlow. And he promised that too. So we all rode on happy, my Lord Wilmot and I thinking it merry sport that Master Evelyn saw not that our requests were made but in mockery but took our gravity for tribute to his immortal fame.

I was told afterwards that this same Master Evelyn was indeed a famous man, but what the devil he is famous for (except for being careful to turn up at Brentford after the fight was over) no one could tell me; and I wonder that I have talked so much about him, for he was a vain and shallow fellow, and lacked both understanding and wit; and though I saw him several times else, I never heard him say a thing worth remembering; but we avoided each the other when we decently could, for I do not think he admired me in the way my Lord Taafe did, but only in the sneaking way of the Puritan who would not know what to do with me had he had the chance.

The King all this summer was beset by doubts as to what were best to do to recover his crown; and his two chief plans were that he should go for Ireland, where my Lord Ormond had

an army and many loyal Catholics, or to Scotland, where the
Covenanters promised him an army would he but swear to the
Covenant. 'Twas a hard choice to make, for neither a Catholic
nor a Covenanting King would recommend himself to the people
of England; moreover, the Irish are a savage race, and as for the
Scots, why, as the King said, a man must needs hesitate before
he puts himself into the hands of folk so Christian and Godly
that they had sold his father to the executioner. So mostly he
was resolved for Ireland, and he told my lord of Ormond so; but
he must needs wait for money to accomplish the journey. And
meanwhile he was so beset by advisers, all clamorous and hot,
that he knew not which way to turn; and what with the Queen
intriguing for him to marry Mademoiselle, and beseeching him
not to imperil his life by gathering an army to fight brute Cromwell; and what with the conflict within himself between invading
for his crown and living quiet and easy with me, the poor lad
was hard put to it to remain gay.

And in the end, he put flaps over his ears to shut out the
argument by going off to Jersey as the only place in his dominions
where he could fly his standard; and we spent the winter there
in great content—or, rather, such content as was possible by
reason of the Duke of York insisting on coming with us, and
the cares of State following the King wherever he went. Still,
though he had little money, we had a tolerable routine in Jersey;
the King could mingle with his own subjects, and be affable to
'em, and they deferential to him, which was comforting to a
crownless young King. And sometimes he had sport with his
guns and his dogs; and I was happy for the last time in my life.

My mother wrote to me whiles I was in Jersey, to tell me
that Cromwell had put out a warrant for my arrest, and others'
too, as if there was some treasure missing, belonging to the
State, or so he pretended. And later I heard that my aunt Gosfright was clapped into prison over the business. But there was
no proof, and she was not in prison long, and Cromwell has
never rightly known what the devil happened to the jewels that
were filched from under his warty nose in the Tower. Colonel

Barkstead questioned me closely about the treasure when he had
me prisoner in the Tower in the year fifty-six, but I knew not
what he was talking of, for I never saw nor handled a jewel of
it, and so I told him, but he stole my necklace for a reprisal, as
I shall tell.

My mother also wrote that she had heard tell of my being
brought to bed of a boy without being wed, and she was shamed
that it should be so, but I wrote and told her private that I was
wed to the King, but that the King durst not acknowledge me
for his throne's sake, and that she should be proud to be the
grand-dam to a King's son who would be King himself in the
fulness of time. It was not that I believed it, but I said so to
comfort my mother, who was sore distressed at the thought of
her daughter's misfortune.

'Twas a great grief to me that I could not visit my mother,
nor carry my Jacky for her to see; and I could not write her
many letters neither, for trusty messengers were hard to come
by, and if a man took a letter who was not in Cromwell's pay,
he was like as not to be cotched by Cromwell's men, and then
all was lost.

And that (said Mistress Barlow) is the true story of the year
I passed in Paris and Jersey as the King's mistris, loving the
King with all my heart, and bearing as humbly and as meekly
as was within my nature the innuendoes of the men who would
have had me if they could and the sneers of the women who
had not been found out. It is the true story, as I hope to be saved.

VI Breda: Disillusion

(July 1650-December 1651)

THE KING AND I (said Mistress Barlow) were almost as happy, oft-times, during our year together in Paris and Jersey, as when we first came together. But there was a shadow over our love— as well as my grief that he would not make an honest woman of me—and that was that the King was determined to strike a blow for his throne, and could not rest easy and comfortable with me. One thing happened, though, that settled his problem of whither to go, and that was that brute Cromwell slaughtered so many of the Irish that even his appetite for blood was assuaged, and then he took to shipping thousands of the poor Irish to Barbadoes as slaves, until there was no army left to fight for the King; so the only place the King could go was to Scotland, to swear to the Covenant and be crowned King and then to descend on England with a Scots army. But I was afeared for him, for the last time there was a Scots army in England with a King, the Scots sold the King to Cromwell and Cromwell cut off his head, and I trembled to think what they might do with his son. But though I pleaded with him that the whole plot was to get him into their power so that they might plunder Cromwell of more bags of gold, all the considerable men of affairs he most trusted urged him to go, and in the end he went.

Everyone knows how brute Cromwell beat the Scots at Dunbar

and the King's army at Worcester [3 September 1651], where Leslie's Scots stood aside and hardly struck a blow, and how my poor master was obligated to run like a hunted hare; and though he often tells the story of his adventures now, and laughs over 'em, yet the thought of his danger always makes me weep.

But, though the King did go for Scotland, and was crowned there, too [1 January 1651], he delayed a long time setting out, and that was because he was loth to part with me. He durst not take me with him, he said, because the Scots were over-Godly, and would look sideways at him did he come provided with a mistris. So he left me at Breda to await his summons to White-hall to join him there.

He fixed on Breda to be near his sister Marie; yet not so near as to cause her embarrassment; and soon after I arrived there, I found I was breeding again. So I lived very quiet, paying for my necessary expenses with the money the King had provided, and a little from the bounty of the Princess Royal, who was childing herself. And when I was brought groaning to bed of a King's daughter, I named her Mary, after that same gracious Princess, and after the King's mother, too.

'Twas whiles the King was in Scotland that his poor sister came to her time of trial, and a bitter time 'twas, too, and more than her deserts; for her young husband, whom she loved dearly, was snatched off sudden by the small-pox, and a week later she was brought to bed of a sickly boy. I was greatly grieved that I could not go to her, and encourage her in her labour, for I was her friend and her sister-in-law as well; but my own time was nigh, and I was told that 'twould not be proper for the King's mistris to pay a call on the Princess Royal at such a time, so all I could send her was a message, for which she told me she was grateful, and was sorry I had not come.

Another reason I was sorry for her was that her babe [after-wards William III] was so sickly and ill-favoured, and one not likely to grow to man's estate and carry on his father's line; but I was not altogether sorry, neither, that my by-blow Stuart should be a more handsome and plumper and more lively lad than the King's legitimate nephew. And I thought it a shame that this puny boy should be in the royal line of succession, and should come to the throne, belike, should his three uncles be killed in the wars without heirs and he outlive them—which is not likely to happen, but is the law—while my son, earlier born and conceived in love following a marriage in church, even though an unlawful one, should be debarred.

The King writ to me but twice whiles he was in his kingdoms; he could not write often for all the letters he received were read first by the godly Scots before he saw 'em, and all the letters he sent were writ for him by those same Christians and haters of loving women. So 'twas only when Dan O'Neile, or some other messenger he could trust, sailed for Holland could he write in his own hand, and even then, he told me, he must needs be mighty cautious, lest the messenger be waylaid by the Scots and his papers ravaged from him. And pieces of paper were but paltry substitutes for his loving arms, even though he named me therein: 'migh owne deare luv, migh wyf'. And mostly I heard only travellers' tales of my master, and little comfort were they.

So for a time I was afeared that he would marry the Earl of Argyll's daughter [Lady Anne Campbell] for 'twas credibly bruited abroad that his intention was for that. But he 'scaped that dreadful fate, and I was glad. 'Twould have been a fate worse than death, he told me later, for she was an ill-favoured wench, and sour by nature like her father [Archibald Campbell, 8th Earl and Marquis of Argyll, 1598-1661], though her eyes did not reflect her mind by looking two ways, as his did, yet she was given to ravings and was nigh demented. Alliance with the Campbells might have found the King favour with the Scots, but 'twould not have hit the mark with the English, so when the Scots ran away at Dunbar [3 September 1650] the lady's hopes were dashed, and my husband was saved.

One day, as I drew near my time and was sore dreading the pains I was to suffer in consummation of the King's desire for my body, came to me my Lord Taafe, to enquire after me on behalf of the King, and to see that I had all things necessary for my condition and my lying-in, as indeed, thanks to the Princess Royal rather than to her brother, I had.

My Lord Taafe was civil enough, seeing that he knew not I was married to the King, and thought I was his mistris, but he was too merry over the business for my liking, and he had no tact neither, for one thing he said which displeased me was that he did not know why the devil His Majesty employed him on this errand, for though he knew as well as any man at Court about the getting of babies, he knew no more than a new-born baby's backside how they are delivered, no, nor cared neither. Which I said was mighty heartless of him, for if men had to bear the pangs of childbirth, they would not be so eager to beget children. But he said that that was how the world was made, for men to get children and women to bear 'em, and for his part he would not have it different.

But the thing he said which was a great grief to me, and made me mighty angry, was that the King had sent him, so he averred, to kill two pheasants with one shot, for that after he was satisfied on the King's behalf as to my comfort, he was charged to do the same for Mistress Betty Killigrew. And when I asked him who the devil Mistress Betty Killigrew was, and what the King had to do with her, he said that, on his honour, he had had the same to do with her as he had had to do with me.

And when I would not believe he spoke the truth (for this was the first I ever heard of Mistress Killigrew) and taxed him with it, he said that, on his honour, the two of us were like to be brought to bed so nearly simultaneous, that the King must have done our business both on the same night. Or if not the self-same night, 'twas the same week, and there were wagers at Court which of the two of us would be delivered first.

Indeed, I had no choice but to believe him, so that when he left me I lay down and wept with shame and grief and rage that my husband and master should have betrayed me so.

But that was not the only wound I had to suffer whiles the King was across the water, for when my Lord of Bucks [George

Villiers, second Duke of Buckingham, 1628-87] escaped from
England after Worcester fight, he came into Holland to pay
his respects to me and to give me news of the King. Though the
news I was dying to hear—where the King was and that he was
alive and safe—he could not give me, for at that time no one
knew. The Duke fought at the King's side during the battle,
and when all was lost they rode out of the burning city together;
but they were so large a party that after a few miles they
separated, the Duke going one way, and the King and Lord
Wilmot t'other. The Duke dodged by devious routes to London,
and hid there in disguise, and then took ship for Holland, and
so was safe before the King and Lord Wilmot arrived in France;
and for some time no one knew where the devil the King was.
And what was fortunate for us all was that bloody-hearted Cromwell did not know neither.

I was glad indeed to see the Duke of Bucks, and to hear from
his lips news of the King, and I was grateful to him for his
civility in paying his respects to me. He told me that all was
not well between him and the King, who had been playmates
in boyhood, and had kept very close in Scotland, since the godly
Scots had sent all the King's other companions away; and they
rode knee to knee in the army that invaded England, yet they
had not agreed well, for the King had rejected the Duke's
counsels, or had accepted them only with reluctance. I was not
convinced, hearing only the Duke's side of the case, that he was
necessary in the right of it, for my Lord of Bucks was ever
stiff in his opinions and oft-times wrong, or so the King told
me. Yet so incensed was I by the King on my own account,
that I allowed the Duke to rail at my master and his. There was
one thing I remember that rankled particular with him, and
that was, that when the Scots army marched into England, he
had advised the King to send the Scots general, Leslie [David
Leslie, afterwards 1st Baron Newark c. 1610-82], about his
business, and appoint the Duke of Bucks commander-in-chief in
his stead, which the King would not, saying he was too young.
Which the Duke held was a great wrong done him by the King,

and cost him the battle too; but when I told the King that later, he said he would sooner have given the command to his horse than given it to the Duke of Bucks.

And so hot was the Duke against the King that I could not contain my own distress, and thinking to discover some fellow-feeling in him in my loneliness, I cried out in my indignation that the King could get another woman with child (meaning Mistress Killigrew) when he had his wife willing to satisfy him. And when the Duke smiled at this as not believing the truth of it (I mean, that I was his wife), I must needs confess the whole story of my marriage—of the church and the chaplain and the responses and the ring. And I told him too, that after the ceremony, I knelt and prayed for a blessing on our union, but I did not tell him that I prayed to the Virgin Mary.

The Duke listened grave enough, but when I had made an end he told me that, in truth, the story was no new one to him, for he had heard it before, and from the King's lips, and what I said but corroborated what the King had told him. And when I railed at the King for revealing what was agreed to be a secret between him and me, the Duke said he doubted that the King had told anyone but himself, for the Duke was his sole intimate in Scotland, and he had laid it on him to keep it privy, too.

So I said that hereafter I should hold the Duke to witness that I was the King's wife; at which he looked at me curious and enquired did I know who that reverent-voiced chaplain was; and when I admitted that I knew him not from Aaron, he told me that the fellow was a play-actor that the King had engaged to play the part of a minister and read the marriage service over us. And when I protested that I did not believe him, for my husband would not play such a dastard trick on a trusting maid, he assured me, on his honour, that 'twas so, and that 'twas a trick after the King's own temper. For the King had said that as my heart was set on a marriage service as like as could be, he had engaged the actor to read the service because an actor would read it more reverent than any chaplain, and so I would be the better pleased.

But I said that was damned nonsense, for 'twas a chaplain I
had stipulated for. But, seeing I was like to burst into tears at
the thought of the deception, the Duke axed what the devil it
mattered who read the service, so long as 'twas read well and
sincerely, for the marriage was not lawful anyway, and I knew
'twas not lawful from the start.

But it mattered to me; for though I was obliged to concede
in my heart that 'twas reason he spoke, yet I was not comforted,
for 'twas trickery and deceit to fob me off with a play-actor,
and I saw then why there was no blessing on my marriage, for
'twas a mockery and a sin, and a desecration on a Holy Church,
even though only a Catholic one.

The Duke went away and left me burning with shame and
indignation; and I came to the belief that the King had not
entered the marriage with reverence and piety as I had done, but
had been laughing in his sleeve all the time, and had not loved
me as I loved him, but had consented to the ceremony and turned
it into play-acting, because only thus could he enjoy my body,
which was all he desired of me; so he had tricked me into submitting to his lusts, and when he had had his fill of me, he had
turned to Mistress Killigrew, and made a whore of her, and had
occupied his time in Scotland making whores out of trusting
wenches, I shouldn't wonder, and that was why he had not
overcome brute Cromwell, for he had gone chasing after light
women and not minded the business of the army; and I decided
he had been served as he had deserved, and the devil take him.

And my shame and my indignation burned within me so
fierce that, when the King returned to Paris from England, 'twas
all I could do to refrain from reproaching him immediate; and
I confined my letter to saying that, since nought mattered to me
but his safety, I was not so much distressed that he had not
regained his kingdoms as overjoyed that he was safe.

He replied that, Faith! he was overjoyed, too, but it had
been a damned near thing and he doubted not but that Cromwell's men were still dragging the ditches of Hantshire for him.
He went on to say that he had arrived near naked, without a

shirt to his back or a sou in his pocket, and that he had had to borrow a shirt from my Lord Germaine in order to dine with the Queen his mother, and that she was so pushed for money that she had presented him with a bill for his share of the dinner, so that he might as well have dined at an inn, though he could no more pay his mother's reckoning than an innkeeper's.

Though he added that he was dying to see me, he did not command me to come to Paris, nor say that he would come to me, neither; so in a few days I writ again, to say that I wondered that he did not command me to bring his children to him, since his son had grown mightily since he crossed the seas, and his daughter he had never seen. He answered, but after an interval of two or three weeks, that indeed he did long to see 'em both, and their mother more so, but that he was plaguey short of ready money, and so occupied with Affairs of State that he was obliged to forego all pleasures whatsoever until a more convenient time, but he hoped I was in good health, and he promised to send me some money as soon as he received some.

I thanked him for his kind wishes and his promise, since I could not trust myself to say more; and I did not hear a word from him for several weeks; and then, when I thought he had quite forgot me and that I am an abandoned woman indeed, he sent me forty pistoles, which was like a fortune to me as I then was situated. But even so, I would rather have had his presence and his love.

And what wrought up my anger was, that he sent the pistoles by my Lord Taafe, who did not neglect to assure me of his continued devotion to my interests, and who went on to say that he hoped I would regard him as the King's representative and deputy in all matters. And when I asked him had the King commanded him to represent himself so, he replied that, on his honour, the King's commands were to assure himself that the lady was content, and that he knew of only one way by which a lady could be made content, and he was accordingly at my service.

To which I replied that nought could make me content save

the presence of the King himself, and as for my Lord Taafe, I thought but little of his honour so long as he did not fulfill his previous promise to oblige me in every particular by carrying out the express commission I had laid upon him at Paris.

My Lord Taafe was not one whit abashed at that, but protested that, on his honour, he was going to the devil as fast as he could, and no man among His Majesty's subjects was proceeding faster, but, if I were indeed sincere in my desire, I owed it to him to accord him some assistance in the matter.

But I told him he must go to the devil his own way, and we parted as good friends as before. Whether he next waited on Mistress Killigrew, and whether he was more fortunate with that poor wretch than he was with me, I know not, nor cared, for I never saw her in my life, nor wished to, neither, and if my Lord Taafe did not know where to discover her, I could not have directed him.

When he was departed and I was left lonely, longing for the King, distressed that he was burdened with cares and counsellors and I was not nigh to comfort him, and sore with envy to suspect that he had found some other female to sully, and wretched myself because I did not know whenever I might see him again, I could not but brood over my misfortunes; and the sending of my Lord Taafe on this errand made me think on the previous occasion of his acting as the King's errander, and, as I brooded, my resentment and bitterness and jealousy overcame my resolution to be kind and patient to the King, and I writ him another letter, which 'twould have been preferable to have chopped off my right hand than writ it, but so angry was I that my pen spluttered all over the paper, and my tears fell on the ink and moistened the words with great blots, but 'twas legible enough for him to comprehend the purport of it.

For I related what his Grace of Bucks had told me concerning the chaplain and the trick that had been played on me, and I said that I wanted him to know that I knew how he had deceived me and made a whore of me who had loved and trusted him so; and then I told him what my Lord Taafe had told me about Mistress Killigrew and her bastard, and I made an end by asserting that if one punk was not sufficient for him, yet one seducer was sufficient for me, and asking what the devil he meant by sending my Lord Taafe to deputise for him, when he knew well that I was the King's alone, since I loved the King with all my heart and with all my soul and with all my body, and was and ever would be obedient to his every desire, save that I would not prostitute myself to his messenger nor to any man else, since I belonged to the King only.

And when I had put my name to that, I added a post scriptum to the effect that if those same idle-tongued, ill fellows at Court who had wagered whether Mistress Betty Killigrew or Mistress Lucy Barlow should be delivered first of one of his bastards, had laid more wagers on whether my Lord Taafe had been successful in his endeavours to have to do with me, he could tell them that, whatever my Lord Taafe might say, on his honour, to the contrary, he had been sent away with a flea in his ear, and that if the King sent an hundred impudent Irish men to deputise for him, they should all fare likewise.

The King writ back immediate that he was mighty sorry that my Lord Taafe had offended me, but that he had most evident exceeded the instructions confided to him, and had been most severely reprimanded for it; and that all the King's servants had been reminded most express that Mistress Lucy Barlow must be treated with the utmost consideration and respect, and must not be insulted in any way, neither by word nor by look; and as for wagers, there were no such wagers about me; and finally, that he honoured me for my constancy, admired me for my spirit, and loved me for myself; and the dearest wish of his heart was to see me soon and to demonstrate his love for me.

But he did not send for me to go to him to Paris, though I could have travelled at little expense to him; and I wrote back at once to say how sorry I was for what I had writ in the heat of my shame and loneliness, and that I begged he would tear up my letter and forget it, for I loved him and would always love him, and would rather be his whore than any other man's wife, and that could I only be with him, I would be submissive to his every wish.

He did not reply for some time, and then he said that I could best accommodate myself to his wishes by remaining where I was, since he was too plaguey poor to provide for me at Paris; but I think the truth was that he had another trusting wretch there—though he had yet to cast his eye at Mistress Catherine Pegge—and had no use for me, since all he wished of me was my body and not my love.

And I believe, too, that his mind was poisoned against me by malicious stories, for I had many backside friends at Court, who resented my monopolising the King's attention before he went for Scotland, and who considered, and with some justification too, that but for his solicitude for me, he would have married his big-nosed cousin Mademoiselle and got his hands on all her wealth and used it, if not for recruiting armies and bribing Parliament men to recover his kingdom for him, at least for paying fat pensions to his shiny-breeched followers. And in particular the Duke of York was my enemy, for the reason which I shall presently relate, and the Duke of York was never nice in his regard for the truth, and doubtless spread some fine tales of me to bedaub my reputation. . . .

So I tarried in the Low Countries, miserable indeed, repenting of my sin in succumbing to my desire for the King's love, and repenting too of my folly in giving way to my natural rage and spite, and so making him irritated and impatient with me, although I loved him so that I could have forgiven him anything had he but been kind to me; and wishing I was dead, and hoping I might enjoy his love again, and realising that I must live to care for my children, who were his children also.

And that (said Mistress Barlow) is the true story of how I lived alone and virtuous in Breda, and bore a daughter to the King whiles he was in Scotland, and how I quarrelled with him when I learned he was unfaithful to me. It is the true story of this unhappy time, as I hope to be saved. And though it is shame to me to confess, yet the recital of the misery which came upon me to punish me for my sin may perhaps persuade some poor maid who reads my story to give no heed to the promises of lying seducers, but to preserve her virtue and her honour.

VII The Low Countries: Opportunity

(January 1652-November 1654)

To ME AT BREDA one day (said Mistress Barlow) comes my long-faced brother-in-law, the Duke of York, and he says he comes from his brother the King with a message; but when he is seated in my chamber, he delivers me no message, but begins to compliment me on my face and my figure, and in particular upon the shapeliness of my legs, the which he has never had the occasion of surveying, but which his brother the King has commended to him.

And when he arrives at last at the point of insinuating that I allow him the privilege of inspecting those same legs, I tell him flat that I will not allow of it, not even if the King has commanded me to show 'em. For my legs are the King's pleasure, and no man but the King shall see 'em. The Duke then says that 'twill be to my advantage to be more generous with my charms, and when I ask him, is it the King's message to me that I shall lift up my petticoats so that his message boy shall have the privilege of gloating over what is reserved for His Majesty, he concedes that 'tis not so, but that his brother has indicated that he is a-weary of me, and that he (the Duke) can have the reversion if he is so minded, and if I am so minded likewise.

So I enquire innocent of the Duke if he is so minded, and he admits that he is, but that 'tis only prudent to inspect a property before taking up the option.

The which renders me speechless with rage; and my Welsh blood mounts to my face so, that he supposes I am blushing with maiden modesty, for he sits there simpering with the satisfaction of conquest, and ogling me so that, had I a bodkin handy, I had run him through on the instant.

When I have recovered my breath, I tell him straight that I am the King's love and mistris, and no other man's, and that I do not believe the King has said he is a-weary of me, nor that the Duke is welcome to me neither; and that I wonder at a royal prince attempting to seduce an honest woman with such lies.

The Duke exclaims that I am a little spitfire, and that he admires a woman of spirit; to which I say that he is a young whore-monger, and I despise and hate men of lust. By which I think I have persuaded him the business he has come on is hopeless; but it does not, for he comes and sits beside me with all the confidence in the world, and puts one arm round me, and tries to squeeze my bosom, and t'other hand to my skirt, and tries to buss me, etc.

At which I wrench myself free, and give him a great whirret across the ear, and pull his hair, and am like to have scratched his face, too, only he turns it aside; and he falls sprawling; and is still on his hands and knees, looking mighty rueful, and with his sword all tangled up with his legs, when I ring the bell and command my servant to show the gentleman the door.

And so this lascivious boy departs with a monstrous great red mark across the cheek where I have slapped him, and a mighty rent in his coat where it has caught in his sword. And he has nought to say for himself at this time, but he says a-plenty later, as I learn to my cost. Never again did His Royal Highness, the Duke of York and Albany, etc, pay me the dishonour of his suggestions, but from that time forward he spread malicious lies and insinuations about me, for he hates me as much as I hate him, and he is unscrupulous to boot.

For evidence came to me that stories were spreading behind my back, and that I was regarded as no better than an whore, though I reserved myself strictly for the King and would not allow any other man familiarity, though plenty wished to have the same, and 'twas freely buzzed about that they did. For ever and anon some fine gentleman I had never saw before would come belabouring my door at night, raising a clamour and awakening the neighbours, and roaring for service, and would not accept that mine was a respectable house and that Mistress Lucy Barlow was not open to all comers. And when at last my landlady or my servant turned them away, they departed mouthing oaths, and enquiring of the dark heavens what right had I to be hoity-toity and to pick and choose my gallants, and were not one man's ducats as good as another's?

When I asked such fellows who it was who said I took any man's money, they said 'twas the common talk of the town; and when I demanded the name of one man who lied so, they would not say—until at last one more drunken than the rest did confide that 'twas the Duke of York had given him the recommendation, saying that although my legs were ill-shapen at least my favours were cheap.

So, because of the dirt the Duke of York flung at me, I was obligated to move to another town, but 'twas hard for me to obtain lodgings, for the Duke of York's inventions followed me wherever I went, aye, and preceded me too, so that when I enquired might I lodge at a house, I was oft-times told to my face that I was known for an whore, and might not lodge where decent people were; and although I denied that I was a common slut and was indeed the King of England's mistris and his alone, I was told that 'twas well known that many fine gentlemen visited me and stayed closeted with me upwards of an hour or more; and when I said that they were servants of the King or of the Princess Royal, waiting on me to pay their respects and to bring me money and messages (as was indeed the truth), I was told that be damned for a tale, and I could go and tell it to my aunt Eliza, for she might believe it, but no one else would. In a word, I was told to take myself and my bastards to the devil and not to waste honest folks' time. And I was mighty angry and humbled; and I could not forbear to cry out at the King for my bitterness and my humiliation, for he was the cause of it.

'Twas difficult, too, to obtain a servant who would be clean and respectful to me; and more than one slut departed sudden, stealing my goods, and saying they feared for their reputations did they serve an whore, though, were the truth known, they were more whores than was I, being promiscuous and submitting themselves in dark church doorways for money.

In the summer of fifty-four comes Daniel O'Neile, and glad am I then to see his long-lipped Irish face and hear his never-pausing brogue, for he brings me the wherewithal to pay my debts; and, what is more, he gives me the hope that I may see my husband again. For he tells me that brute Cromwell has made a treaty with Mazarin, and stipulated in it that Charles Stuart (as he calls the King) must be expelled from France, but King Louis has sugared the pill with a handsome present and the promise of a pension. So my husband has money in his breeches pocket, and the freedom to travel, and he intends for Germany and a holiday with his sister.

But when I ask, does this change in the King's fortunes betoken for me the felicity of his company? the subtle Irish man will say neither yea nor nay, but honeys me around with a cloud of sweet words, so that I am rendered both hopeful and afeared. I am not entirely minded to confide in Daniel O'Neile, for though I know the King trusts him, yet that is no reason that I should trust him too, and though he has never attempted to have to do with me as my Lord Taafe has, yet he is an Irish man, and sure, he talks too much. I think, indeed, that he aims at a different target and has no thoughts for any woman but Lady Standhop [Catherine, Lady Stanhope, afterwards Countess of Chesterfield and Mrs Daniel O'Neile]—and that only because she keeps a good table and satisfies his demanding belly.

So I feel myself safe to plead with him for his aid, saying that, could the King but see me again, and refresh his memory with the sight of my face and the sound of my voice and the presence of my love, he would be sure to love me again, and could Daniel O'Neile but bring me into the way to a meeting with the King, the act would earn him the King's gratitude for ever; and though Daniel O'Neile seems a trifle doubtful at first, yet in the end he concedes that it may be so. And the plan he suggests is, that he should escort me to Liége, there to await the coming of the King, for he must pass through there on his way to meet his sister at Spa.

So I set out for Liége under the care of this Gentleman of the King's Bedchamber, but when we arrive at the inn we find that the King has passed on a full two weeks before. At which Mr Subtle O'Neile looks quite out of countenance, and protests that he wonders at the King leaving Liége so soon, for he had certainly thought to meet him there. I do not know what to do now, and Daniel O'Neile cannot think what to suggest, for 'twould not be fit for me to go chasing His Majesty all over Germany; but while we are debating what were best to do, there comes to Liége Sir Henry de Vic, who has been attending on the King at Aachen, and who is on his way home to Brussels, where he is the King's Resident.

I counted myself fortunate to make the acquaintance of Sir Henry de Vic, for he was a gentleman who treated me respectful as a lady should be treated, and neither fawned on me as one who, an she wilt, could speak with the King to grant him a favour, nor leered sideways at me as a loose woman whose body was available to any man with the price of it in his purse. 'Tis true, though, that my new friend was not only kind, he was also so venerable that I supposed he had it not in him to do me a mischief. He had, indeed, served King Charles the First as Ambassador before I was born. When I put it to him that I had not the means to await the King's pleasure at Liége yet was afeared to return to the United Provinces where insult awaited me, he offered to escort me to Brussels, and said very fierce, that if any man molested me there he should answer for it with his life. And he put his hand on his sword as he said it as if he was ready to run the man through on the spot that dared insult me.

He had a daughter of his own, he said, and he would regard me as one with her. The which I took for a high compliment, for the said daughter—the final flower of his manhood, as she seemed—still had some years of virginity in her, whereas I was the mother of two children.

That was well enough, and I took comfort at it; and he kissed my hand and paid me compliments that were agreeable and not insinuatory, and altogether he was mighty civil. And the only reason I did not look upon him as a father was, that he was older than my father, and kinder, and not lecherous nor swear-spoken. The day we set out for Brussels he told me that 'twas his birthday, and bade me guess how old he was, and I said I thought he might be fifty—looking at him careful the while, as if I was estimating from the wrinkles round his eyes and his white beard, but in truth wondering if he might take fifty for gross flattery and if sixty might be nearer the truth and yet under enough to please him, for indeed he was most valetudinarian to my young eyes; but he said he was, I forget exactly what, but on the begetting side of sixty, so that I satisfied him enough, unless, like all men, he was a liar. I remember I calculated that he must have been born in Elizabeth's reign, which always seems a mighty long time ago to me.

Indeed, Sir Henry de Vic was so eaten up with rheumatics in the legs that it occupied him five minutes, almost, to hoist himself out of a coach or into one; and when he dragged himself up stairs he was puffing and blowing like a March wind, so that on a hot day 'twas quite refreshing to stand in the way of it. And I was used to thinking, in my innocence, that the reason he never looked nor spake insinuatory to me was, that being so venerable, he had long since put aside thoughts of fornication, and was incapable of it.

Meanwhile, Daniel O'Neile departed for Aachen, or for Spa, or wherever the King was, leaving behind him a cloud of windy speeches and promises to procure for me the King's invitation to re-union. But he was a mighty long time obtaining that same invitation. And when I had been abiding in Brussels for some weeks, Sir Henry de Vic paid me a visit at my lodgings, and came puffing and wheezing up the stairs so that he announced himself long before he appeared; and spread himself over a couch the while he recovered his breath, and then he paid me some compliments on my appearance and then fell silent.

As I do not know why the devil he has come, but suppose he has something of import to relate or suggest, and perhaps from or about the King, I keep silent too, being eager to hear what he has to say.

At length he says he would have me know that he is a widower, for his poor wife has died some years ago. Which I say I am aware of, and am sorry, for he is a polite and well-spoken old gentleman.

Then he observes that every man needs a wife, and I agree that no doubt a wife has her uses.

He says he misses his late wife greatly, and I say that no doubt a man who has had the bounty of a good wife must miss her sorely when God takes her.

Then he puts it to me, do I not think that every woman needs a husband, and I agree that a woman is unlucky if she does not find one, as I know to my cost.

Then he asks me, have I never thought of marrying, and I reply that I have never thought of marrying anyone save the King, for I have never loved any man but the King, and could not think that marriage could be happy without love.

To which he responds, that he is older than I, which is very true, and has had more experience of the world, which may or may not be true, and that in his experience marriages without love at the first are often happier than love marriages, for if a maid marries for love, she is like to be disillusioned, men being deceivers ever, whereas if she marries for a home and a position, she is more likely to get not only what she bargained for, but also be agreeably surprised to discover her husband more tolerable and affectionate a companion than she anticipates.

The which I concede is likely enough, if indeed the husband does turn out to exceed the maid's expectations; but for my part,

I say, I love the King with all my heart and have never thought of marrying anyone else.

At which he falls so silent (save for his panting breath) that it seems we shall sit speechless like fools until my maid brings in the candles and discovers me in the dark with a man—and even though the man be as old as Methusalem, yet he is still a man and subject for scandal—so, not being able at the moment to think of any other subject which may interest the old fellow, since his mind seems to run upon connubiality, I ask him, has *he* never thought of marrying again?

He replies that for some years he has not, by reason of the fact that he has not believed he will ever meet a woman he can bear to see in occupation of his deceased wife's place; and I say that such a sentiment is mighty laudable of him.

Then he says (becoming pathetic) that of recent months his loneliness has been impressing itself upon him, and he has felt a craving for female company and comfort; and I say I can well understand that, (for, I think, but do not say, so venerable a gentleman will soon have to take to his bed and will require a nurse to bring him broths and wipe his sweating brow, et cetera).

But (just as I, viewing myself as a loving and innocent maid, cannot understand how the world can think of me as a common slut, so this old man cannot perceive that to me he is but a foolish actor lingering hopeful on the stage long after his part has been spoken) he betrays no awareness of such a thought, and goes on, boastful, but wistful, too, to say that, though he has passed the half-century, yet he has always lived cleanly and healthy, and he is still strong and able, both in body and mind, and good for many years yet, that he can conduct business with the efficiency of a young clerk, and ride all day and not be tired, and that he can give a good account of himself in a sword-fight, still, if needs be.

To which I say, laughing but not spiteful, that, sure, marriage does not so much require the pricking of a bully in a duel, as the giving of satisfaction to a woman in bed; and he proclaims at once that no doubt he can still do that too.

So then we both fall silent, for I cannot yet perceive in what quarter the wind blows, and I am mystified as to the purport of his remarks. So at length I say that I suppose he has looked with favour on some likely lady and has it in mind to pay his addresses to her, and is seeking my opinion whether 'tis wise to marry again at his age, and whether I think the suit of a man of fifty and some will be likely to prosper.

He seizes on that, and exclaims, all eager and with a great explosion of breath, that I have pricked my man right to the heart, for that is exactly what his purpose is. So I say that he must be aware that he is a man of high repute and honourable employment, that he possesses the confidence and favour of the King, that his manners are agreeable and his person clean and breath sweet, and that any woman who is no longer a young maid and does not sigh for a lusty young fool she can mould to her own desire, will be likely to accept him with gratitude for God's goodness to her.

At which, to my utter astonishment and dismay, the poor old gentleman suddenly flops down on his rheumaticky knees before me, entangling his coat grievously with his sword as he does so, and imprisons my hands in his clammy grip and begins kissing them through his ragged moustachios, and implores me to marry him.

'Twould be the greatest honour of his life, he says, would I condescend to be his wife.

Though I am a woman, and a Welsh woman at that, I cannot find words for my emotions. Indeed, so accustomed am I to being told to my face, by men and women alike, that I am an whore, that I have no notion that any respectable gentleman would think of marrying me.

So he kneels there kissing my hands and calling me his duck and his darling and his guiding star, etc., and other pet names I forget, and makes a proper old fool of himself; and I am half laughing at him and half sorry for him, for I do not know how to tell him the thing is impossible without offending him, which I would not do for the world, for no man has ever paid me such honour and kindness.

But at length, since it is clear that, if I do not speak and put him out of his suspense, he will either stay on his knees on my chamber floor until his old joints stiffen into permanent bends, or else will take my silence for blushing modest assent to his proposition, and so exacerbate my difficulty, I tell him, but gently, that I have the greatest honour and liking and respect for him, and no man has ever paid a wretched slut a greater compliment, but that he must know the thing is impossible, by reason of the fact that I am married to the King.

'Married to the King!' he cries, in a voice wherein astonishment and disappointment wrestle to come out on top.

I am obliged to concede that 'tis not by lawful marriage, but by lovers' vows and every shackle and desire, and by the fact that my children are the King's, too; and therefore I am His Majesty's entirely.

He says, still kneeling there, that he knows well enough that I have been the King's mistris, and that my two children are the King's, but he has heard of no marriage, lawful or otherwise, and he has not heard of any believable ill of me, neither; that he admires and respects me, and, in short, that he loves me, and would cherish and protect me, and that, as the mistrises of Kings are like to settle down and marry some time, he has hopes that I will do him the honour to allow him to take care of myself and my children henceforth.

'Tis when he mentions my children and the caring for them that I wonder, has the King persuaded him with promises of promotion to take me off his hands, so that he will not be further at the expense of providing for me; but I think I wrong Sir Henry there, for when I ask him, does the King know of this scheme to rid him of his abandoned mistris? he answers, sincere enough, so that I believe him, that there has been no mention of me at all in his conversations and correspondence with the King or with his Court neither; but that he comes to me at the first, for he is consumed with love for me, and will marry me if I will have him, let the King think what he will. And as for my being the King's *abandoned* mistris, he does not know for a fact that I am, for Daniel O'Neile has not said so; but he is aware that the King has not visited me for long, and he has heard tales that, although His Majesty has gotten no regular mistris since he escaped from Worcester fight, yet he is not living in a monastery neither. The which I know well enough.

So I tell Sir Henry de Vic that I am very sensible of the honour he has done me, and that I will treasure it and respect him all my life long, but that the thing is impossible, for I have pledged myself to the King, and though he be unfaithful to me, yet I can think in that way of no man but he. I am the King's while the King lives, and perhaps for ever after, should God take the King and leave me forlorn.

And as he still crouches there on his poor knees, holding my hands tightly, but not kissing them any more, and looking up at me with his sad eyes with the wrinkles round 'em, I say to him, merrily (not laughing at him, but to make him smile), that he must arise, for he has been on his bended joints long enough, and to no purpose, neither.

He nods sadly at that, and I am alarmed that he is about to shed tears, for he screws his eyes shut, and puts his head down, and gulps; and then he grips my two knees so firmly with his two hands (which are mighty strong for so venerable a body) that I almost cry out, for I think my refusal has turned him mad, and I am afeared for my honour; but 'tis only that he must grip something tight to unbend his bones and haul himself to his feet, and when he is upright again (after digging a sharp elbow into the front of my thigh so that I am bruised there for a week after), he apologises between panting for breath.

And I perceive that if ever he does get himself another wife, 'twill be one of her wifely duties to straighten him out whenever his senile impetuosity ties his rheumatic limbs into knots; and that if indeed he ever attempts to have to do with her in bed, why, the puffing from his exertions will blow her right out on to the floor.

So I think I will not marry him, even if the King commands me to do that same.

I supposed he would depart then to weep over his disappointment (and maybe to tax his brains to find some more compliant and mature female to comfort his breathless years), and leave me to my astonished laughter; but he did not. He was a determined old gamecock, and he asked, did the King accord him permission to press his suit with me, would I allow him to address me on the business again?

To which I answered that I did not know what my feelings and plans would be should the King formally abandon me, but that he was welcome to consult the King (if only to demonstrate that I spoke truth when I asserted that I was the King's), though I could not by no means promise that, did the King give him permission to try his luck a second time, he could count on achieving his desires.

So Sir Henry de Vic kissed my hand all reverent, and puffed his way downstairs, and all the trees waved in the air as his breath was expelled in the street; but he left me in the very devil of a dilemma to know what to do for the best, both for myself and for my children, whose care has always been my chiefest concern after my love for the King. Perhaps I had agreed to sacrifice myself for their sakes and become the good knight's lady on the spot, had I not been well aware that Sir Henry de Vic was as impecunious as I was myself.

And that (said Mistress Barlow) is the true story of my miserable life in the Low Countries during the years fifty-two to fifty-four, and of how the King's brother, His Royal Highness the Duke of York and Albany, made dishonourable proposals to me and became my enemy, and how a respected and honourable baronet wished to have me for his wife. 'Tis the true story of my wretchedness, as I hope to be saved, and I tell it for an example to trusting maidens who may be tempted into sin by the hopes and passions of love without foreseeing the punishment that must inevitably follow.

VIII The Hague: Realisation

(November 1654-April 1656)

THE NEXT I HEARD of Sir Henry de Vic he was gone for Cullen [Cologne], where the King was with the Princess Royal, to ask the King's permission to marry Lucy Barlow (said Mistress Barlow). But simultaneous I heard that the Princess was returning to The Hague, and I was resolved to go thither and ask her advice about the venerable gentleman's proposals, and to plead with her to persuade the King to provide an establishment for his wife and children, so that I should not be molested by vulgar fellows set on by the Duke of York, and by his malignant lies about me.

The Princess Royal greeted me kindly, and wrote to the King on my behalf, and the upshot of it was that the King commanded me to attend on him at Cullen. So thither I went, taking our two children with me. The Princess provided me with a fitting escort in the persons of a wealthy English merchant and his wife and family, who were for Cullen and had some spare seats in the coach they had hired and were not unwilling to employ the same to enable them to talk broad for the rest of their lives on the journey they took with the King's mistris and his children; and, indeed, they were more agreeable and civil to me than many a great lord or Master Evelyn would have been; but what they said about me to their friends afterwards I do not know, though

I suspect 'twas not much to my credit, the world being what it is, and a fallen angel more gossip-worthy than a virtuous woman.

When I waited on the King my husband at Cullen, it troubled me to observe the lines of worry on his forehead and about his mouth; but he was so over-joyed at the sight of me that all my resentment melted, and I stood there trembling, his for the taking. He told me at once that he realised he was a big fool not to have sent for me long since, but he had quite forgot how handsome I was. To which I could not forbear saying that I supposed he had seen a-plenty of other wenches since he had sailed for Scotland; and he admitted that that was so, but protested that he had seen none so beautiful as Lucy Barlow.

There was no gainsaying the man, and he had his way with me, body, and mind too. So that, at the first, I thought that all was restored between us.

But there were with him at Cullen those that were in no wise glad to see the King's mistris, and they protested that 'twas impossible to provide me with lodging in the King's house. So I had perforce to lodge apart from my husband, which was not convenient for the restoration of confidence and trust. But no doubt that was their intention.

The King and his advisers were big with plots and plans for the recovery of his kingdoms, and there was a mighty deal of talk and letter-writing and going to and fro; and I could do nought but sit patient and await my lord and master's pleasure. And though he visited me often, yet something had departed from our love for each other, for I was beset with enemies, who whispered lies about me, and whether he believed them or not, he had his doubts, and he would not acknowledge me as his wife.

Sir Fatguts Hyde [Sir Edward Hyde, first Earl of Clarendon] worked himself to a shadow persuading the King that the English would not have him as King unless he had a born Princess to wife, and there was nought I could do on t'other side. So, for the most part, I subsisted wretched and apprehensive in Cullen.

'Tis true, when the King came to me, he came merry and

AW   H promise-crammed, bounding up the stairs four steps at a time; and there was passion still in our love; but there was not trust. And too often he departed in anger—which was my fault rather than his.

For so overflowing were my wrongs, and so sensitive was I to my position, and so angry with him that he had taken a trusting and innocent maiden and turned her into a harlot for all the world to mock at, that I could not resist railing at him and demanding my rights, so that he rarely found solace with me, though often enough he took his pleasure of my person, and then for a while I was content and he was satisfied.

I own that 'twas a great stupidity in me that I could not prevent my temper spitting out my complaints, for he had his bellyfull of anxieties and troubles, and he knew not where to turn for money for his necessary expenses, though he took good care to see that I and his children had a crust and a roof—so 'twas my duty to show him kindness and patience and love, no matter how he treated me, nor how often he betrayed me with some light woman.

And perhaps 'twas my own fault that he succumbed to the wiles of wanton baggages, for he went to them seeking the comfort he found not in me; yet I am sure he has never found one who loved him as I do.

One error I made was to complain of the Duke of York to him, for 'twas necessary to his plans for the Duke and him to lie buckle and thong, and the Duke was but a boy and headstrong and prone to take umbrage and to protest and rebel, so the King refused to reprimand him, no, not even over the wrongs of his wife. So I had little satisfaction there, for though he denied he had sent the Duke soliciting to me, nor that he had said he would resign me to the Duke were I willing, yet he conceded that on some occasion he might have extolled my hidden charms to the Duke so as to whet his boyish lascivious appetite, and, though he promised to speak to his brother and to command him to cease spreading malicious lies about me, yet he did not do so; and indeed, said he, how could the Duke know whether my legs were ill-shapen or no if I would not allow him to see 'em?

At which I wept, and said he was cruel, and that he had not mocked me when I had had my hair sheared off and wore boy's apparel and risked life and liberty and prison fever in his service; so he turned serious at that, and kissed and cossetted me, and dried my tears, and assured me that my legs were the handsomest he had ever seen—the which did not please me much, for what business had my husband to set up as a connoisseur of female legs, and comparing other legs with mine? But he was so merry and kind and ardent that I was afeared he would get me with child again; only at that moment I did not care what the devil he did to me. For I loved him so, I was always eager to surrender all to him.

But when I pleaded with him to have me permanent at his Court, and to take me with him wheresoever he went, so that all the world should see that I was the King's mistris, and no common slut, he grew uneasy, and said that, Faith! for himself he would like nothing better, but that soon he would sail for England, and belike there would be fighting and no place for a lady; and that whiles his plans were maturing he would be on the move so, and lodging hard, and often in such wretched and cramped quarters, and with so many men to provide for and to find roofs for, that 'twould not work. And he was so occupied with business and plots and plans and schemes and letters to this man and reports from that, etc., etc., etc. that really he had no time to call his own, and a man would liefer be a dog and catch fleas in the sun than a King, did he know what a King's life was like.

And when I said, why not give over trying to be a King, and marry me and live easy for ever after, and let the Duke of York be King and have all the worries of it and serve him right, he prated about his damned duty; and there was no shifting him from that, for if ever a man was impregnated with the sense of duty, and ever determined to mortify the flesh to do it, it is this same husband of mine, His Gracious Majesty, King Charles the Second, King of England, Scotland, Ireland, France and

Wales, Defender of the Faith and seducer of innocent maidens.

But when he had given over lecturing me upon his sacred duty, he conceded that there were other things in the world beside it, and the most important of them to him, he said, was Mistress Barlow; and she would always be so, provided she did not get confused in his mind with necessary but dull business. For, surrounded as he was by spies and flatterers and grave men of affairs, 'twas necessary for him to come away and forget all with me; and were I at his side and mixed up in his thoughts with Affairs of State, he would make of me a dutiful habit rather than an occasional joy. Whereas now, whenever Master Fatguts Hyde granted him leave to take a holiday and pay his respects to Mistress Barlow, he threw his hat in the air like a schoolboy, and came galloping mewards overflowing with tenderness and excitement and love. So 'twas preferable, he said, for me to abide in one place where he could find me when his plots and plans and schemes were in abeyance.

I said that 'twas not consonant with his dignity, nor with mine neither, that he should ask Master Hyde for permission to visit me; but he assured me that such was but a mode of expression, for he never mentioned me to the Chancellor of the Exchequer, but he did consult him when he desired to take leave from his interminable conferences.

And he went on to say that the pot was like to come to the boil soon, and he would be aboard ship any day now, and so 'twould be best were I to return to the Low Countries, and pitch upon some convenient city there to await his triumph. At which I protested that I would endure any hardship to be with him; but he said I must obey him, and obey him I did.

To sweeten this bitter pill, he gave me a pension warrant, all sealed and signed by himself and by Sir Edward Nicholas, Secretary of State, for five thousand livres a year, to be paid quarterly, from the July previous, which was when he left Paris. I accepted this promise because 'twas the best I could have, but I doubted it would be paid regular (which it has not been), for I know he has little money, and little chance of more, and many calls on his purse, and I would liefer have his love than his money.

'Twas a plausible and sweet-tongued tale he told me, and I dissembled that I believed him, though I believed him not. For I suspected that half his schemes and plots were aimed not at regaining his throne but at seducing some big-mouthed wench who had told him straight that she would have him exclusive or not at all. The which I think was proved right enough, for when I parted from him at Cullen, he remained there for two years and more, and never went across seas to fight brute Cromwell for his crown; and my Lord Taafe told me that at Cullen the King and all his Court passed their time dancing to the fiddlers. And 'twould puzzle even my clever husband to dance without females to partner him, and I had taught him to my cost that there are other things he could do with females than dance with 'em. But I was obliged to swallow my spleen and try to show grateful for such favours as he offered me; and though I knew not for the fact that he was unfaithful to me at that time, yet I know full well that his ardour would not permit him to live continent.

No doubt 'twas because the King would have it so that the Princess Royal provided me with lodging at The Hague; and I was glad to be near her, for her company was always agreeable; she was in ordinary merry, and always kind. But I was sore to be dismissed by the King and my heart was full of foreboding. With his honey tongue no longer tickling my ears, and his coaxing looks no longer beguiling me, I could give thought to my wrongs, and they were well nigh unendurable. So when the Princess asked me, would I write to the King, she would send my letter enclosed in hers, I said that all I had to say to him was to send him my humble duty.

'Twas common knowledge that Sir Henry de Vic was proposing for me, and Princess Marie made merry over it, but that did not distress me, for she knew well I loved her brother and him only, and 'twas a family joke that the venerable old man should seek to supplant him.

Sir Henry did not long remain at Cullen after I arrived there. He soon perceived that it was a sleeveless errand he went on, and after he returned to Brussels he did not write to me nor communicate with me again. Indeed, he found himself a more convenient woman, as I heard, and a thankless dance she led him. I was sorry to hear of her, for he was a kind old man, and he made me a great and a sincere compliment. But I was not sorry the business came to naught, for I do not think I could have endured marriage with him. He was burnt down to the socket and no sort of use to a wench of twenty-two save only to give her an honourable name. That I would have valued, but the fact was that I felt myself so wholly the King's that I could not endure the thought of another man's embraces, and I shall hold to that, I think, until I die.

The King would not tell me, when I enquired of him subsequent, what he said to Sir Henry de Vic in answer to his request to marry me, except that he had expressed wonder that a man who had escaped from bondage should run around, chains in hand, begging people to fasten 'em on again; but I think, from what my Lord Taafe said to me once, that there were those about the King who intimated to Sir Henry that it would displease a man who must be powerful when the King returned to his own (meaning the Duke of York), should he make an honest and respectable woman of me, for the Duke was resolved that the world should think me a common prostitute, because I would not submit myself to his lusts and so become what he said I was but what I was not.

I think, too, that the word must have been passed to Daniel O'Neile that his attempt to find favour with the King by escorting me to Liége had misfired, and had made him enemies among those who found it inconvenient to their ambitions for returning to England that the King should persist in loving me; for when he came to The Hague his oily Irish manner was swamped in vinegar, and I could not find that he was even pretending to be my friend.

The Princess Royal had it in mind to go for Paris to visit her mother, whom she had not seen for ten years or more, and I think Daniel O'Neile came to The Hague from the King on some business connected with the visit; he remained there for some weeks, but whether because the King's affairs detained him or because he had the freedom of my Lady Standhop's dinners, I knew not. When he paid his respects to me, I said I wondered that he had brought no provision for my necessary expenses, for my Lord Taafe had written to say that the King had my needs ever in mind and would send me a supply as soon as his own purse was replenished. But Mr Subtle O'Neile pulled his long upper lip at that, and said he knew nought about a supply for me, and he wondered that my Lord Taafe should promise me something that was not in the King's power to perform in his present circumstances, for his allowance was promised or hypothecated for months ahead.

This was hard news enough, but the thing that he said that caused me most disquiet was, that the King was resolved to have his son put to a tutor and sent to a school. To which I replied that nothing would give me greater pleasure or satisfaction than this assurance that the King intended to acknowledge his son and to equip him for a gentleman, but that the boy was too young for a school yet, and should remain in his mother's care a while longer; and that the King knew well I was having the babe properly instructed in the principles and practices of the Established religion; and taught to mind his book and to read and write both in French and English, and was myself teaching him manners and deportment, and how to make a leg to ladies; and that, as soon as the King provided me with the wherewithal, I intended to have him taught to manage a horse and a sword as a gentleman ought.

But Daniel O'Neile said he conceived the King had resolved to engage his own tutor for the boy, and would shortly desire me to send Jacky to him for the purpose. And at the suggestion that my dear son, the image of his father and the pledge of his father's affection for me, should be wrested away from me, I waxed angry, and I told Mr Ingenious Subtle O'Neile that I would never consent, never, and that if the King would but have me about him, he was welcome to have my son and my daughter also, but if not, not. The which did not please Mr O'Neile, as I could see, but I did not care about that, for I was besides myself with rage.

And no wonder, for I was mighty sick at the time, racked with pains, and taking physic. The physician said he could not see that there was aught ill with me, except perhaps that I was worried sick, and I think he was right; but oft-times since I came away from Paris I had lacked the wherewithal to buy nourishing food, and often had I gone hungry to bed that my children might have their little bellies filled; and now I was in such despair at being sent away by my husband the King that I could have turned my face to the wall and died were it not for my duty to his children.

The Princess Royal had been mighty solicitous for me in my plight, and when she went for Paris, she charged my cousin Tom Howard, who was her Master of the Horse, and an officer in the English Regiment at The Hague, and Lady Standhop's son-in-law, too, to see that I wanted for nothing necessary for my health. So presently, praise be to God, I recovered.

But the Princess Royal's kindness sprang back at me and caught me in a stick and added to my misfortunes. For at this time I had the mischance to be served by a slatternly maid who robbed me and told infamous lies about me when I sent her packing after I came home unexpected one afternoon and found her naked in bed with a gallant.

Who he is I know not nor care, for 'tis dark in the room, but so incensed am I that I seize hold of him by his bare shoulders and roll him out of bed on the floor, and order him out of the house all mother-naked as he is; and I tell him that I will not have my house turned into a bawdy-house for any man; and when he retorts that any house wherein I am is necessary a bawdy-house, I grab up his sword and threaten him so fierce with it, that so alarmed is he and so formidable do I appear in my Welsh rage, he runs into the street with his shirt round his neck, and falls bottom over tip on the doorstep; and I fling his jacket and breeches after him, and he for shame's sake is obliged to retreat into a doorway and put 'em on before he departs swearing down the street.

When the villain has gone, I turn to my maid and cry shame on her for turning my respectable lodging into an whore-house, but she retorts saucily to me, saying 'tis merely a case of like mistress like maid, for if she is an whore, then I am doubly an whore, for she has never borne a bastard, whereas I have borne two.

Whereupon I beat her and bid her put on her clothes and begone to the gutter where she belongs, and so she departs weeping and rubbing her sore backside where I have beat her, and vowing vengeance, too.

I was mighty sorry I had not rid myself of the maid sooner, for I learned after that she had often entertained men in my house when I was abroad taking the air, and so had earned it the reputation of ill-fame, which was held as a mark against me and caused me much distress. For she went about the town, saying 'twas she had found me abed with Tom Howard, and that she had left my service voluntary on account of my ill way of living, and that I had tried to silence her by thrusting a bodkin into her ear whiles she lay a-sleeping, and further that my illness since I came to The Hague was nought but miscarriages, brought on deliberate; which was all malicious lies, though many believed 'em, and there were many gallants in the town who had had to do with her in my lodgings and had pointed the house out to one another as a cheap bawdy-house.

When this fairy-tale came to the ears of Tom Howard, which it did because Daniel O'Neile asked him joking if he thought he was as good as a King now he lay as good as one, he gave it the lie, but the trouble was that he had lately married my Lady Standhop's daughter (who was governess to the Princess Royal's infant son, but who had gone for Paris in attendance on the Princess), and her father, my Lord Kirkhoven, Lady Standhop's husband, is one of the most considerable men at The Hague, and (whether he believed Tom Howard's denial or not) he thought it was not fit that his son-in-law should be talked of in this way, and he threatened to expel me from the city, using the false witness of my dismissed maid as a pretext, the which was most unjust, for 'twas I who was the innocent and wronged party.

In my trouble I had no one to put my case to but Dan O'Neile, and to do him justice he persuaded my Lord Kirkhoven to withdraw his threats; and he stopped the mouth of that malignant maid, too, though it hurt me that he did it with a bribe, for I could have found a better use for the money, and what that slut deserved was a public whipping.

And another thing that displeased me about the business was, that Dan O'Neile took it upon himself—for I am sure the King would never instruct him so—to warn me to live quiet and peaceable and not to keep dragging the King's name into scandals; to which I replied indignant that no one more than I desired to live quiet and peaceable, and that, would the King support me in the manner that was my due, and allow me access to his Court and Person, so that all the world could see that I was the King's acknowledged mistris, there would be no trouble from me, nor none about me, neither. For 'twas the King's own contriving that I was not everywhere treated with the honour and respect which was the right of the mother of his children.

But as to that, Daniel O'Neile would say nothing, and that was ominous, for never did I know him at a loss for words before; but whether it meant that the King had resolved to abandon me, or that Daniel O'Neile was resolved that he should abandon me, I could not tell. And Daniel O'Neile went away then, and I have not seen him again nor wished to.

And that (said Mistress Barlow) is the true story of how I went to Cullen to plead my case with the King and of how his solemn advisers persuaded him to send me away with the promise of a pension which he had not the means to pay, so that I must needs live in penury and loneliness, with no friend to turn to in my troubles. 'Tis the true story of my punishment for my sins during the years fifty-five into fifty-six, as I hope to be saved.

IX London: The Tower (May-July 1656)

ABOUT THIS TIME (said Mistress Barlow) my aunt Gosfright writ
to say that my mother had died and had left me a legacy of
£1500; she had not named me in the written will, but she had
told my uncle Gosfright, who was the executor, to give me the
money private, lest brute Cromwell should seize it by reason
of my being the King's mistris. My uncle Gosfright had died,
too, and my aunt said that, would I come to London, she would
tell the lawyers to pay me, for she was administering the estate;
but she durst not have me lodge in her house, for she was afeared
that if Cromwell learned that I was in London and in communi-
cation with her, he would have her put in prison again.

'Twas hard to make up my mind whether to go to London
for my legacy or no, for although I needed the money, yet I
was afeared that if Cromwell cotched me he would put me to
the torture, knowing I was the King's mistris and might reveal
his secrets; and although I was confident I would not confess
even under torture, yet I was not privy to the King's plans and
could not reveal any even had I wished, so I should be tortured
with no gain to anyone.

In the end, I wrote to the King and asked for his commands,
and he answered that I should go, and that, indeed, I could do
him some service, for I could carry messages to trusted friends
in England, and bring back messages too, and he would provide funds for the journey and for my subsistence in London.

For my better protection, he said, the messages would not be written, but verbal, and I should learn them by rote, and they would be in a key, so that even if brute Cromwell forced me to repeat 'em to him, he would be none the wiser.

I wondered that the King should trust me when he treated me so shamefully, but I durst not say so; and indeed he knew me so well that he was confident that I would gladly give my life for him, though I could not control my temper when he came to me. So I wrote to my brother Justus, who was studying at the Temple in London, and prayed him to come to Holland and escort me to London to collect my legacy. And in due course he obtained a pass from the Parliament and came. 'Twas kind of him to aid me, though it turned out to his misfortune, as I shall relate.

While I was preparing for this visit (the which I thought would occupy me two or three weeks at most) and wondering how to discover some reliable person to tend my children in my absence, one Prodgers came sniffing round my lodgings. Ned Prodgers was (and, I suppose, still is) Groom of the King's Bed-chamber, which is the polite way of naming the chief pimp; and it was his office to carry out any unsavoury business which wanted an unscrupulous and cunning rascal. He is a sinister fellow, and I have never liked him, or had aught to do with him could I avoid him; I had good reason to mislike him then, and better reason later. On that occasion he made himself as affable as he could, but his smile made me shudder, for he smiled as I have seen the hangman smile as he adjusts the rope around some poor wretch's neck, and I knew that Prodgers' smile was like the pirate's black flag and signalled that there was dirty work in the offing.

So when he enquired, had I made arrangements for my child-ren to be tended whiles I was beyond seas, and said he was acquainted with a worthy couple who would be mighty suitable for the purpose, I was much afeared, for I suspected that he purposed to steal my boy from me, and the girl too, perhaps. I asked, did he come from the King on this business, and he said he did, for the King was most solicitous for his children's welfare; and I said, so was I, and that I had agreed with a good woman in Antwerp to care for them, and had indeed already paid her the money. That was a lie, but when you negotiate with a liar (for such prying Prodgers is), 'tis no use telling him the truth, for he will not believe you; and indeed, he did not believe me, for he asked me where the woman lived and what her name was, explaining that, did I not return as soon as I anticipated, the King would be able to pay her any arrearages needed for their upkeep.

I was sure then, that he was lying, for the King is not the man to pay arrearages can he avoid it, and I began to think that perhaps one of the messages I was to take to London was to be passed on to Cromwell, so that he would arrest me and put me in prison so that I would not come back, and then the King would have my son. And the next thing would be, that the Duke of York would pay some bully boy to slit his throat. So I told Master Prodgers that I had mislaid the address, but would send it to the King. With which prying Prodgers had to be content.

But he looked round the room mighty curious, as if to see where I had hidden the children, only I had not hidden them, for I had not observed his coming (otherwise I would), but they were abroad with my maid.

This visit affrighted me so, that I resolved to take the children into England and have them with me there, rather than allow Master Prodgers and the Duke of York to get their hands on 'em. So I sent my maid sudden in advance to London, where Prodgers could not bribe her, and then I left my lodging at The Hague and betook myself to Antwerp, as if to place the children in the care of the good woman I had spoke about; and, indeed, I found a Dutch woman who would serve my purpose, for she spoke only Flemish, which I speak indifferent, and I was able to make a bargain with her to look after the children whiles I was away (or so she would understand) and yet take them with me at the last moment and tell her she had misunderstood me, and I could pay her something to make up for the mistake.

Then, if prying Prodgers questioned her beforehand, she would say, yes, they would be in her care.

When my brother Justus arrived, I would make all speed to be gone, but the King sent word that he desired to come to Antwerp to see me; and come he did, and stayed a day and a night, and mighty merry and tender he was, so that 'twas almost like the early days of our love, ere he went for Scotland.

But I could not forbear taxing him with his scandalous way of living, and scolding him for the monstrous procession of women he lay with and the getting of divers of them with child; but he protested that 'twas all a tribute to me, for his sole hope and ambition in all he had to do with women was to discover one he could love as he had loved me, so that he could be sick again with love and desire as he had been with me.

But I told him he would not find love promiscuous, but only by loving one woman alone and loving her truly all his life, as I loved him truly. To which he replied that that may be so with women, but 'twas not so with men; and seeing I looked sad, he went on to comfort me by protesting that though he had quite forgot most of the brisk wenches who had shared his bed but two or three years since, for one wench was much like another, especially in the dark and horizontal, yet he always carried the memory of me with him, and he still loved me in his heart, though not, he owned, as passionate as at first. For all feelings grow old and change with the years, and you cannot expect a man to approach a feast, even though he be hungry, for the thousandth time with all the zest and appetite he came to the first with.

And I owned, for my part, that I did not love him quite as I had loved him at first, for I had trusted him and believed him then, but even now when I understood him better, and knew he was false to me, he was still the only man in the world for me, and would be so for ever.

I did not trust him, and I suspected that 'twas a farewell embrace he was giving me, and that he had arranged for me to be betrayed to Cromwell and thrust into some stinking prison to die of fever. Yet so loving was he, and so mightily did he stir me, that I was more than half minded to confess all my doubts and suspicions, and to hand the children over to him and go willing to the fate he had prepared for me, and thus to serve him with my death. But had I spoken so, he had not conceded that his plans were for my death. And then, as I was meditating in what manner to confess, he made some mention of his brother, and when I thought on the Duke of York, I hardened my heart, and resolved to take the children to safety and defy the Duke, for I knew I should be a great fool to trust the King.

But I did all I could do to satisfy and to honour the King, for I hoped that, were I mistaken and the King was treating me honest and sending me on an important mission, and did I carry it through successful, then he might be able to throw down brute Cromwell, and mount his throne, and then, did it please His Majesty, I could be acknowledged Royal Mistris, and accommodated suitable in Whitehall. For I well understood now that never could I be his wife and Queen (not whiles the Duke of York lived and his tantrums ruled all), and so low had I sunk that I should have been content to have been his mistris, provided I was treated as such, and could see him often and serve him when he pleased to notice me.

Yet still I doubted I should leave the children with him, for he had brought them sweetmeats, and romped with them, and charmed them as he charmed everyone, and Jacky loved him, and so did the girl. And I said to the King, after they were put to bed, that I was disquieted to be told by Daniel O'Neile that the King would have the boy, as if he were to be put to a school, for he was of tender years, not yet seven, and the person I loved, next to his father, in all the world. But, said I, if he is to be educated to be a royal prince, then I will gladly hand him over to whomsoever the King will appoint, provided only that I have access to him and he is not brought up to forget nor to despise his mother; but if he is to be brought up a bastard, why, I can do that myself.

At which the King laughed, and said that, Faith! his son

must be educated for a prince, and sit in the House of Lords when his father came into his own; but that if I desired to retain the boy a whiles longer, I could do so, and we could plan his education together when he was a trifle older. The which contented me for a time; but I did not hand the children over; for whiles the King was with me, came Prodgers to the landlady, and questioned her about them (as she told me subsequent), and I knew that I had judged aright, and that death in prison was to be my portion and my reward for having loved the King.

But though I was willing to give my life for the King, I was not willing to sacrifice my babes' lives for his brother. So I bade the King my husband and master a tender and affectionate farewell—and if I kissed him deceitful, sure, he kissed me deceitful too—and then I carried my children straightaway for Flushing and on to the vessel, and so, with my brother Justus, set sail for England and my death, as I thought.

In the cabin came to me my cousin Tom Howard, saying that he wondered to be told that I was aboard ship, for he had not known I was sailing for England. 'Twas not a pleasant appearance, but I made what best of it I could, and told him of my legacy; and he said he was on private business for the Princess Royal, and he made himself mighty agreeable to Justus, and before I knew what was toward, they had fixed for us to lodge together in some rooms hard by Somerset House, which Tom Howard alleged were central and cheap—as indeed they proved to be.

Because I had been so sick when I came from Lyme in the year forty-eight, I was sore afeared of the perils and discomforts of the sea, but no such evacuations marred my comfort this time, and the tarpaulins had no need to ask me if I was looking over the side to see what wood the ship was made of; and the children were not sick neither.

My maid, Anne Hill, joined us in our lodgings, and we lay mighty quiet for a week or more, keeping a good table and hiring a coach for our necessary outings, but not seeking to display ourselves.

My cousin Howard went abroad more frequent than I did, and where he went and what he did I know not; but I was made easy by his absences, for they provided the occasions to attend to my own commissions; and whiles he was abroad, divers friends of the King visited me and I delivered all my messages, and received others in reply. But what the devil they all meant, or indeed whether they meant anything at all, I had no more idea than my aunt Eliza. 'Twas evident to me that, whatever the King's plans for my fate were, he had enjoined on his followers to use every respect to me, and to treat me as a lady of quality and one who had the King's ear and respect; for they all acted so, and some bent low and kissed my hand with more than ordinary ceremony; and one poor lad, to whom I offered wine, snatched the cup from Anne Hill, and proffered it to me on the knee, as if I were the Queen. At which Anne goggled mightily. Why the lad did thus, I knew not, except that perhaps, knowing me the mother of the King's children, he took me for Queen. And Almighty God knows I ought to be!

Many of those who visited me asked particular, might they see my son, and when he came into the room, they marvelled, and exclaimed, for he was mighty like the King when he was the same age. At which I took much comfort.

My private business was transacted also, and I saw my aunt and was very merry with her; and I was paid my legacy of fifteen hundred pounds, and I bought with it a necklace of pearl, the better to carry the value over to the Low Countries; but that was stolen from me, as I shall tell.

Then, sudden, one evening, when we are all together in our lodging, come Redcoats trampling, with warrants to search our possessions, and arrest us all and carry us to the Tower. So I know then that I have guessed aright, and that 'tis the King's plan to have me put out of the way. And yet I do not understand why Tom Howard should be clapped up as well, except that he has been carrying messages for the Princess Royal.

I plead with the corporal to allow my children to remain in the lodging in Anne Hill's care, for I am afeared of what the girl may say were she arrested and interrogated, since she is well aware that I am the King's mistris; but the soldiers will not heed me, but take us all, and would use me roughly, only my cousin Howard speaks for me and protests that I am cousin to the Earls of Suffolk and Leicester, and must be treated as such. He says he is the brother of the Earl of Suffolk, and they allow him to retain his sword on the word of a gentleman that he will surrender it to the Lieutenant at the Tower; and he whispers to me to be of good cheer, and all will be right in the end.

My brother Justus is less willing to suffer arrest, and speaks them sharply, so they fling him down the stairs, and march him off with his hands pinioned behind him, poor lad; which the sight of distresses me. But the soldiers are gentle with the children, and permit Anne Hill to carry them to the coach they have prepared for me.

'Twas a miserable night I spent alone in the Tower, for the children had been lodged with Anne, and where Justus and Tom Howard were I knew not. I was afeared of the torture, not the pain of it, for a woman who has borne children knows she can endure great pain and survive to be merry afterwards; but for fear that my arms and legs and fingers might be broke and twisted out of shape, so that I might no longer soothe and delight the King, should his plans miscarry and I escape to join him again. But as for revealing his secrets, why, I know none to reveal.

Two days I lay alone in the Tower, awaiting the fate prepared for me and for my children. Beer and victuals were brought me, but I was told nothing. I implored those that brought the victuals to tell me where my children were; but all they would say was, that they were well. And with that I must be content. I had no one to comfort me but God, and He was not much comfort neither, for I knew I had been sinful, and though I prayed for mercy, yet I could not think myself forgiven and believe that succour was at hand.

On the third day I was brought before Colonel Barkstead, the commander at the Tower, and commanded to explain myself. When I looked around and saw no rack nor thumbscrew, nor no pair of masked torturers standing grimly against the wall, I took courage; but then the thought was that I was to be hanged for a spy; and that cheered me somewhat, for were I to be hanged for the King's sake, why, I should fly straight to Heaven; and sure I had no use for this world had the King abandoned me. 'Twas not death I abominated, but mutilation; so I answered the Roundhead cheerfully enough for one in my position.

I told him truthfully that my name at birth was Lucy Walter, and that I hailed from Pembrokeshire, where my brother Richard had but lately served the Lord Protector (meaning Cromwell) as High Sheriff; and then I said what was not true, that I was a married woman and my name was now Barlow. I admitted that I had borne a son to Charles Stuart (which was what these barbarous men call their King), but said that son was dead, and that the two children I had with me were by a Dutch sea-captain who had been cast away in a storm. I said I was married to this captain, and I had not seen the King for two years and more, and had come to London to collect my legacy, but had not gotten it yet. I said that because I feared they might take my necklace from me, as indeed they did. They claimed 'twas some measure of recompense for the treasure I took to France seven years since. I protested that I knew nought about any treasure, but they would not heed me. And, indeed, from what they told me, they knew more about the business than ever I did. They gave me no redress, neither, though they knew well that if indeed I took treasure to France, 'twas not for myself but for the King. But 'twas no avail; they retained the necklace, and I returned to Flanders poorer than I left.

Another thing they stole from me was my pension warrant, which they printed in their diurnal with derisive remarks.

Colonel Barkstead did not believe the lies I told him, for my maid revealed all, and I cannot blame her for telling the truth, for the poor wretch was mighty frightened to be clapped up in the Tower, and she was privy to the fact that I bore messages from the King. Colonel Barkstead read out to me what she said in her interrogation, and asked me, did I deny it; and I said nought. So I know that she said nought to my discredit, for she said that my children were the King's and that the King maintained me, which was the truth; and there was nought there for me to be kept in prison for, nor to be hanged for, neither.

What my brother Justus said, I know not, but he knew nothing to damage me, and he is a good lad and would tell the truth. As for my cousin Howard, no doubt he did not tell the truth, but I know not what lies he told.

After they had interrogated me and stolen my necklace, I was kept locked up in the Tower for more than two weeks, not knowing what was decided for me; and all I could think was, that brute Cromwell was awaiting the leisure to decide what was to be my fate. I think, indeed, that he was debating whether 'twould serve his turn better to have me strung up at Tyburn or to embarrass the King by shipping me back to Flanders.

I learned later that, whiles I was in the Tower, every one of the people to whom I carried messages was seized; and some of 'em were hanged for turncoat spies, and some were flung into jails and left to rot there, and several were sold as slaves to the Barbadoes. And, indeed, 'twas one of my fears that I was to be Barbadoed, too.

However, that was not my fate. Without doubt, brute Cromwell understood the ins and outs of the business more thorough than did I; and he would not allow an innocent woman to be hanged. Who has ever gotten at the truth in a Court which is a nest of spies and counter-spies and where no one knows what the devil anyone else is up to? Without doubt, there were plots within plots, and some of us were spies and some were dupes and some were unsuspecting martyrs and some were sneaking informers, but who was which I cannot say, except that I was a dupe; and I know now that my cousin Howard was an informer.

The King was well aware that Tom Howard was one of Cromwell's spies, and 'tis my belief that he made occasion for him to sail on the ship with me with the intent that he would betray me and all the men I carried messages to, as if those same men were friends of the King who were no longer trusted, and so were desired out of the way.

My subtle, smiling husband was well capable of a master stroke to rid himself of his importunate mistris and his inconvenient followers; and, from other things I have heard since, I believe another messenger was sent simultaneous with me, but more private, and he carried the real business behind the scenes, the whiles I strutted on the stage to be arrested and flung into the Tower. If indeed 'twas the case that I was but a dupe and a decoy, then I am not ashamed to have served His Majesty in that capacity, for I would serve him as he wills.

For my part, I swear before Almighty God that I was faithful to my trust. If 'twas the case that brute Cromwell perceived the King's game and threw me back over the net to despite him, 'twas none of my doing. I was as ready to rot in jail for the King as to be hanged for him. 'Twas Cromwell's doing that the bad penny turned up again in Flanders.

Another of my worries whilst I lay in prison was that they told me that my daughter Mary was took ill, and that my aunt Gosfright had taken her for tending, and my maid, too; and they allowed I could have my Jacky with me, which was a comfort; but 'twas a cause of some alarm, too; for one afternoon, when Jacky and I were walking in the yard for the exercise, a man came and watched us most intent. 'Twas all I could do to restrain Jacky from running away from me, and perhaps climbing on the walls, for he is an active lad and impatient of control, so I had eyes for nothing but my boy, and I did not perceive the man until Jacky almost ran against him. He was a stout man, red-faced, as elderly as Sir Henry de Vic, perhaps, and yet not bearing himself like an old man. His attire was plain and he wore a hat to shade his eyes from the sun; and what I noticed particular about him was that all his attention was on my babe, and he had scarce a glance for me. The which I was not accustomed to from men, and it frightened me to have a man so set on my Jacky. So I thought it best to go back to my room, though to do so necessitated passing close to that same man. He made me a civil salute, so I dropped him a curtsey, though I knew not who the devil he was, and I passed him without a word. And he, for his part, said nought, and made no motion to hinder us.

But, later, when I enquired who the devil the red-faced gentleman was, I was told he was indeed the devil himself, brute Cromwell. And now that I have seen him face to face, I can say that he is a very brute, but there is something of force in him, for I swear that, had he made suggestions to me such as the Duke of York made, I had not resisted him. I had been as a wax candle in his hands, though I hate him and would have hated myself did I demean myself to submit to his lusts. However, he made no such suggestion, and, please God, we shall not meet again, and so he will never attack my virtue. I am told he has no concern with women now (which is a thing most extraordinary in a man), so I think that men too maybe feel as I felt, and are obliged to submit to his will from the very power of the man's look, be they never so rebellious in their hearts.

'Twas well I knew not who he was, for, had I known he was the murderer of my King, I had spat in his face, though then I had been compelled by the power of his will to surrender all.

Yet what I can say of brute Cromwell was that he was civil to me, which many fine Royalist gentlemen are not.

'Twas a day or two after that, on the sixteenth of July, that I was led before Colonel Barkstead once more, and he told me that the Lord Protector had writ the warrant for my release, and Jacky too. He read the warrant to me, and it gave my name as Mistress Lucy Barlow, and described me as 'Charles Stuart's Wife or Mistris', and Jacky as 'the young heir'—the which was mighty civil of Cromwell, so perhaps my curtsey pleased him. And I perceived then that he came to the Tower to see my babe and to compare his lineaments with what he remembered of the King's, for he saw the King often as a boy, and in the warrant he writ that 'twas clear that Jacky was the King's son for he was very like him. But where he heard I was the King's wife I know not, for I did not claim to be such, but I suppose the coachman who drove us to the church, or perhaps the grave play-actor chaplain, was his spy.

The warrant said that I and Jacky were to be taken aboard a vessel at once and put ashore in Flanders as a courtesy to my husband, Charles Stuart. But Mary was too sick to travel, so 'twas necessary to leave her with my aunt Gosfright to save her life. And though Mary is well and healthy now, my aunt Gosfright has taken her into her house, and she lives there; but now that the King has taken my son, Mary will be brought to me in Paris, and I shall have the comfort of my daughter.

I was glad indeed to leave the grim Tower, where I had lain in such apprehension, and Jacky was glad to leave it, too, for though a babe of his tender years could hardly comprehend the multifarious dangers his mother was in, yet he sensed that I was more than ordinary unhappy; and when we were taken out of the Tower and I told him we were going aboard ship and thence to Flanders, he asked me what the day and the month was, and when I told him 'twas the sixteenth of July, he said, in his child way, he would remember it always, for 'twas the happiest day of his life, the day he was brought out of the Tower of London, and he hoped he never saw the inside of it again, nor the outside neither.

But I reproved him for talking thus, for I said that when the King his father came into his own, he (that is, Jacky) and I would come back to live in Whitehall, and then he would see the outside of the Tower often, but never, I hoped, the inside, except when he became Captain of the King's Guard. At which he changed his tune, and said he would like nothing better in the world than to be Captain of the King's Guard. And indeed, when next the King took Jacky on to his knee, Jacky made him promise he should be Captain of the King's Guard when he was growed a man and we are back in London. The which made Jacky mighty content and wishful to obey his father in all things.

And so I was flung naked on to the shores of Flanders, without my necklace, without my pension warrant, without money, but with my chiefest treasure, my Jacky. I had given my all for the King. I would give it again would he but be kind to me.

Harry Bennet came speedily to me and gave me money from the King for my immediate necessities, and I repeated to him the messages I had brought from the poor wretches who even then were being persecuted for their loyalty. But whether those same messages imported aught I could not tell. The King sent word that he thanked me, and was grateful to me, and was sorry my necklace had been stolen, and he promised me another and a better when he could afford the expense, and meanwhile he would not fail to make provision for me and for Jacky. Indeed, the purport of his message, as I understood it, was that he would do anything in the world for me except have me with him and love me; for he was too occupied turning another trusting maid into a harlot, though whether Mistress Pegge was any better than she ought to have been before she ensnared him, I cannot say. What I know is that she was brought to bed of a son the following year in a month which demonstrated that my husband had had his pleasure of her what time I was shivering in the Tower for his sake.

For Kings are not as other men; they have to bear great responsibilities, and great privileges march with 'em and maybe compensate for 'em. They can command their subjects' service and love, and repay them nought in return, not even gratitude. And I know that I am obligated to love and serve the King until I die; and if he commanded me to go for London to-morrow and be walled up in the Tower by brute Cromwell for his service, why, I would go.

And I know, too, that were the King to come to me with kind words and caresses, yet would I spit in his eye with words, and vent my bitter anger at him for making an whore of me, and for betraying and abandoning me; but after that, I would surrender all to him, and he would have his will of me. For I love that tall deceitful man with all my heart, and I can not avoid it.

And that (said Mistress Barlow) is the true story of my journey to London to collect my mother's legacy to me, and of how that bloody-hearted thief Cromwell robbed me of it. 'Tis the true story, as I hope to be saved.

X Brussels: The Abandoned Woman

(July 1656-December 1657)

WHEN I AND my precious babe were cast penniless and well-nigh naked on the coast of Flanders (said Mistress Barlow) I resolved to proceed to Brussels, for I had information that the King was there. But I found it mighty hard to come to an interview with him. He had brought about a treaty with the Spaniards, and hopes were high at his ragged Court of raising an army of exiles and Irish men for invading England; and the King was so busy with his schemes that he had no time for his cast-off mistris. And some there were about his Court who assured me he was resolved never to see me again. But when at length I forced my way into his presence, he was mighty affable and solicitous, and protested he was mighty sorry to learn of my misfortunes in the Tower, and glad indeed I had gotten out. But conversing with him was conversing with a stranger, almost. It was as though he had quite forgot the days and the nights of our love, and I was no more to him than a handsome wench, and never had been. Which was bitter indeed, for though he said nought to the effect, 'twas plain that I was now an abandoned woman, and with no hope left.

The side-glances I encountered at his Court made it plain that brute Cromwell had won the trick by shipping me back, and it was never intended I should escape. I do not think the

Princess Royal was in the plot, but the King was, for he was quite under the thumb of the Duke of York; for he is persuaded that without the Duke in amity he cannot regain his throne. And at this time there was a great dispute between the brothers. The rights and wrongs of it I never heard, but Harry Bennet and my lord of Bristol were mixed up in it; and the Duke rode away from the Court and went for Holland, and would not come back until the King accepted his conditions, one of which was that Harry Bennet should no longer be his secretary, and another that Mistress Barlow should be thrown overboard; and they found some light woman to amuse the King, and persuaded him that 'twas his duty to agree with his brother in all things.

And I am convinced of this, that this same King, though he is a tender and a passionate lover of women, does not love any woman as he loves his duty, and his duty, so he considers, is to return in triumph to his three kingdoms, and maintain his state there.

I was afeared that the King would take my son away from me, but at this time he made no move to do it, and I knew that so long as his beloved son was in my keeping I was assured of sustenance, and would not be obligated to beg my bread in the streets. Though that was the least of my fears. The chiefest reason why I was unwilling to part with my Jacky was that I loved the babe, for his father's sake and his own too, and I was afeared that, were he taken from me and put to a school, I would see him so infrequent that he would forget me between whiles, or, worse still, hearing tales of me from his school-fellows, he would revile me for a wanton and lay on me rather than on his father the blame for that he is a bastard.

Another thing of which I was afeared was that if he were put to a schoolmaster or a tutor he would be beat, for he is a lively and mischievous lad, always ready for tricks and games, and saucy too (in which he favours his mother, who was ever a saucy wench), and he will not brook correction nor being crossed (in which he favours his father, who is ever resolved to have his own way), and none but myself could control him, and I only with difficulty, so, did he come under a tutor, he would be flogged, and the thought of my merry little babe being beat and bruised filled me with grief, for I would rather be beat myself and bear the pain of it than have my child hurt.

Moreover, I did not think it proper that my Jacky should be beat like other lads, for he is a King's son, and belike will be King himself one day, and 'tis not fitting that a King should let his breeches down for the rod like any common boy. But when I put this to the King, he but laughed, and said that, Faith! he was beat when he was a boy, and it did not do him any harm. To which I replied that it did not do him any good, neither, for if beating had made a good man of him, he had married me proper and made an honest woman of me. Which he did not answer (for he could not), but swung the attack to the other flank by saying that he had seen me beat Jacky my-self; but I said 'twas only with the flat of my hand, and not with a rod, and 'twas nought but a slap when I lost my temper with him and to mark my displeasure because he would not do as I desired, and never to hurt.

So I clung to Jacky and was resolved to retain him as long as might be, though I knew the King would have his way at last. And against the day when he would be taken from me, I was careful to instruct him (though he was barely of an age to com-prehend such) in his position and his rights, and I made him to understand that he was the King's son, and his eldest son too, and that he must conduct himself with dignity and spirit, as befitting his royal parentage. The which he always did, and in particular when he was put to the test he bore himself like a man of courage and resource, as I shall tell later, so that part of my schooling of him was not wasted. Another thing I told him was that, although his mother was not the Queen, yet she was the King's wife, for she had been married to the King, when he was Prince of Wales, in a church and before the altar; and that when the King came into his kingdoms he intended to acknowledge me as his wife and the Queen—for though I do not believe that that is his intention, yet I desire Jacky to believe it and to uphold his rights when he is a man; but I do not know if he understands the difference between legitimate and illegitimate at his tender age, for, indeed, 'tis hard for a grown person to understand, for we are all begot the same way and delivered the same way, whichever side of the blanket we are produced on, and 'tis cruel that a poor mother should be spat upon and called a wanton because there were no witnesses to her marriage.

I was concerned, too, that the boy should understand battles and sieges and the whole panoply and business of war; for I apprehend that he must be a soldier when he comes to man's estate, since it may be that his father, the King, will need to fight for his crown one day—and so perhaps will Jacky, for I fear the Duke of York will play every false card to cheat him out of his rights. So I instilled into Jacky that 'tis his destiny to be a great general and to lead armies into battle, since men were made to fight as women were made to bear children, and I think nought of a man who has not borne arms for his King, nor of a woman who has not endured the pangs of childbed for the man she loves. 'Twas a branch of education which Jacky was not loath to accept, for he never tired of hearing all I could remember of what men who had served in the King's War told me of fights and sieges and marches; and whenever the King his father came to our lodgings, Jacky would climb on to his knee and demand to be told the story of Worcester fight, and of his escape thereafter, which the King never tires of relating; and once, when Prince Rupert was with the King and told of Naseby fight, and of the horse charging and scattering the Roundheads at Marston Moor, why, I could not get Jacky to sleep for a week, he was so excited.

He was well acquainted, too, with my own adventures with the King's treasure strapped round my body; and perchance his baby mind was filled overmuch with stories of fights and escapes and perilous marches, but I was thankful that 'twas so when the occasion came to him later, and at a tender age, too, to display the metal he is made on, and to emulate his father and his mother in outwitting his enemies.

Maybe I have spoke overmuch about my Jacky, but the truth is, he has been the centre of my life since the King abandoned me, and there is no other purpose nor interest in life for me but to train him to be a good man and a great and a valiant one, and able to fight for his rights; and I sometimes think, now that the King has gotten him away from me, that, should I not live to see the King crowned in London and myself beside him, the only thing history will say of me will be, that I was his mother.

To Brussels presently came my cousin Howard. He gave out that he was on the affairs of his brother, the Earl of Suffolk, but I think he was mortally anxious lest he be discovered to be in Cromwell's pay and so be pistolled like that villain Manning. 'Twas as secret from him as 'twas from me at that time, that his treachery was known to the King and that he was written down as too small fry to bother about. His intent was to ingratiate himself with the Court, and his first plan was to pose as my friend, and to persuade me that 'twas none of his doing that I was clapped up in the Tower—the which I suspected not then, but am assured of now—and that, indeed, he was instrumental in effecting my release. Which was as may be. But I allowed that I believed him, for I had no occasion for a quarrel.

But I had been wiser to have sent him packing, for 'twas soon buzzed about that he had had to do with me whiles we were in London, which is a filthy lie, and may I be damned eternally if he was ever more than a cousin to me. But when he perceived I had no influence with the King and that my enemies at Court were eager for evidence with which to persuade the King to cease sending me money for my necessary expenses, he changed his tune absolutely, and boasted that he had indeed enjoyed my favours, and that he was not by no means the only one.

When the lies he was spreading came to my ears, I waylaid him in the street one evening as he passed near my lodging and taxed him with them, and bid him recant. He had with him a little fellow of the country, whom I did not know, but who seemed taken aback at my Welsh vigour. But Tom Howard stood his ground and denied he had spread any lies about me, but had told the truth, namely, that I had always claimed that my two babes were begotten of the King, and that he knew nought to the contrary, for he had never stood beside my bed, nor lain under it neither.

To which I replied that he knew right well that my children were the King's, for the King acknowledged 'em. But he said it proved nothing, for 'twas a wise father that knew his own gets.

At which I grew so angry that the young fellow with him went pale and plucked at Tom Howard's sleeve as if to pull him away. Which action turned close to my hand the handle of his poignard. So in my rage I plucked out the poignard sudden and menaced 'em with it. The little man took to his heels, and my cousin Howard went back a step; but he smiled as if he thought I knew not how to wield a dagger, and held out his hand for it. His smile made me angrier still, and I ran at him and lunged fierce, for I was consumed with fury.

He put up his arm and the point stashed into his elbow and blood spurted out. At which he cried out, and seeing I was about to strike again, he leapt aside and ran for dear life. And at sight of his cloak flying around his heels, and the blood dripping on the cobbles, my anger left me, and I marched indoors with his poignard as a trophy of victory.

Indeed, I was not so content when I grew calmer, but I need have had no fears; for both Tom Howard and his little companion were so mortified at the two of 'em being put to flight by a mere woman that they gave out that 'twas not me, but a man servant or relative of mine that had attacked 'em, and that without warning. So the hue and cry went out for this man, and in course he was not to be found, for he existed not save in the imaginations of Tom Howard and his white-faced little friend.

Yet though I had drawn blood and escaped all punishment for brawling in the streets, I could not feel secure, and I was minded to depart from Brussels and seek some more quiet place. But there came to me Sir Arthur Slingsby, who was my Lord of Bristol's secretary, and was but lately married, and was very

earnest in persuading me to lodge in his house in the park at
Brussels; the which I was glad to do, for Brussels is a most
chargeable town and I was heavy in debt, for my allowance was
in arrearage. Great fool that I was, I trusted the fellow for his
kind words, for I did not know then that he was the very
antipodes of honour.

But I had not been there for more than a week or two before
I discovered that I had gotten out of the pot but to fall into
the fire, for Sir Arthur Slingsby is a black-hearted villain indeed,
and he treated me very ill. He kept me so close, with his servants
watching all I did, that 'twas worse nor being in the Tower of
London; and he would not suffer me to go abroad, nor to receive
letters nor visitors neither—the which he pretended to be the
King's wish, so that I might not cause more scandals, but which
I knew was a lie.

Yet that was not the worst, for when I demanded that he
carry me to the King that I might put my case to him in person,
he said that would not do; but that, would I put my case to
him (Sir Arthur) in a very special way, which he knew I had of
putting cases, then he would ask the King to relent. And I told
him that no man should come between the King and me, for I
was best able to put my own case to the father of my children;
and as for the filthy thing he suggested, he knew 'twas an
abominable lie; and I was so angry that I slapped his grinning
face with all my might, though I was in his power. He looked
angry then, and said that what he was pleased to call my choosi-
ness would do me no good. But he perceived he had catched a
tartar, and so he left me for a while.

Then came December and a plaguey cold December it was; and
with that white December came black-hearted baronet Slingsby,
and sudden demanded money for rent and my victuals and fuel,
though he well knew I had no money, nor could get none
neither, for he would not permit me to apply to my friends nor
to make representations to the King for the arrearages of my
pension.

And when I told him that I had no wherewithal to pay him

rent, and that when he had invited me to lodge with him I had not understood I was to pay rent or aught else, but that he would be recompensed by the King, he swore, with monstrous oaths, that the King had done with me, and would pay me nothing, save only that I handed my son over to his care and departed where I should trouble the King no more.

To which I replied that I would do whatever the King required of me, and reside anywhere and in any condition, provided he gave me what I needed for my necessary expenses and did not separate me altogether from my son, who was all that remained to remind me of him.

But Sir Arthur repeated with oaths that the King was resolved to have the boy, and to lay me by, and that 'twould go ill with me did I not submit. But I said I would not agree until I had seen the King face to face and he had told me his wishes with his own lips. For I would not be cozened out of my son.

He swore the King had resolved never to see me more; and so left me.

And the next night comes Slingsby knocking at my chamber door, and behind him a Spanish officer and soldiers, and bids me don my garments immediate, for I am to be lodged in the common gaol for the debt I owe him, and my son is to be put to a school; and when I will not come out, they force down the door, and the soldiers seize me in my night-gown (and Jacky too, for I cling so tight to him and he to me that they durst not tear us apart); and so we hurtle struggling into the street, where I set up such a bawling and screaming, and Jacky echoes me in his frightened child treble, that though the soldiers understand barely a word of what I am saying, yet they durst not use me too ill, for I persuade 'em the King will have hanging justice on 'em if they lay a finger on me and on the King's son; so the officer is afeared he will have to answer for it with his life, and the soldiers that they will be flogged.

And there in the street, with Jacky still clinging to my breast and yelling at the top of his tiny voice, we set up such a commotion that the people from the houses round about throw up

their windows and demand what the devil all the pother is
about, and a number of 'em come running into the street, and
they crowd around and give heed to my cries, and shout, Shame!
on Slingsby for treating a poor helpless mother so, and I protest
so much and so bitterly, and the mob threatens so, that the
officer and the soldiers are at their wits' end to know what to
do. For they did not bargain for my Welsh temper and my
bitter wrongs giving power to my lungs. And though Slingsby
swears 'tis all done by the King's wish and orders, the good
people of Brussels cannot believe that the King of England can
be so barbarous as to tear a babe from its mother's breast and
put her in the common gaol for no more crime than loving her
son; and indeed, Sir Arthur Slingsby is in mighty danger for
his life, and obligated to retreat into the house for safety; and
the poor young officer is sore perplexed.

Until presently comes the Ambassador's secretary, who someone has sent for, and more soldiers with him, and he gives heed
to my pleas, for he is well aware I am the mother of the King's
children and that the King and Sir Henry de Vic have respect
for me; and he rates the young officer sound and puts him under
arrest, and he sends soldiers into Slingsby's house to fetch out
my goods and belongings, and he lodges me in his own house
for protection for the night.

And so Slingsby's plot to steal Jacky from me failed, for I
retained the babe with me; but I was well-nigh prostrated with
anxiety and grief and passion; and I prevailed upon Monsieur
Mottet (which was the name of the Ambassador's secretary) to
write to the Marquis of Ormond, and to represent to the King
the ill straits I was in, and to say that I desired to place myself
under the King's protection, and would do whatsoever he willed,
provided he told me himself and did not take my child from
me absolutely, and did not require me to lodge with Dan O'Neile
or Slingsby.

There was great exchange of letters to and fro, and I was
much afeared for the outcome; but meanwhile Monsieur Mottet
put me to lodge with my Lord of Castlehaven [James Touchet,

AW   K

Earl of Castlehaven, *c*. 1617-84], who undertook to care for
Jacky and me until the King's pleasure be known, and to charge
me no rent, neither. My Lord of Castlehaven had been in attendance at the Court at St Germain when I arrived there with the
royal treasure in the year forty-eight, and he knew well the
service I had rendered to the King and to the Queen Mother,
and he would not see me abused now. And so I passed Christmas
very quiet at his house, but I knew 'twas but a pause between
battles for me, as it was too for him.

The King's answer was, that he was resolved to have the boy,
for the boy was his and he had the right to him (the which no one
denied, his mother least of all), and that he would do nought
for me did I not submit to his will and yield up the boy. 'Twas
owned that the King had not intended I should be used barbarous,
and that Slingsby had overshot his instructions, which were,
that I was to be used with all civility and niceness, but the
child gotten from me none the less, will I, nill I. But the truth
is, Sir Arthur Slingsby is not capable of using anyone with
civility and niceness, for when God made him His Hand slipped,
and He flung the result down on the earth as a nasty piece of
His work, for the edification of mankind, and to be a warning
to 'em, to be thankful that He had not made 'em as crooked
as Sir Arthur Slingsby.

My Lord Ormond writ, moreover, that, would I surrender
the babe, the King would pay me my pension again, and with
all the arrearages at once, and more when he regained his kingdoms; but that, did I not bow to his will, he would not give
me a groat; and my Lord said too, that the King would send
me a large sum of money, I forget how much but 'twas some
thousands of guelders, did I hand over the letters writ to me by
the King, which proved my rights, and which I said I would
publish to the world were I not paid my pension.

But, since the King would not send for me, nor come to see
me neither, and would not tell me his desires with his own
lips, I was resolved not to surrender his son, nor his letters neither,
for they were all I had to compel the King to grant me the

wherewithal to live; for I could not subsist on his piecrust promises, and once he had the boy and the letters, I could go whistle for my pension.

And, perceiving that 'twould be an ill turn to my Lord of Castlehaven, who had offered me so much kindness, to remain under his protection the while I persisted in defying those wicked men who had gotten control of the King (for I was sure he would not abuse me so, were he able to do what he wished and were he not persuaded that to throw me into the gutter was the only way to house himself in his ancestral palaces), I resolved to steal away from Brussels, and to take my Jacky to some quiet village, where I could leave him safe with respectable folk who would tend him, unknown to the Court, and then to go alone to Bridges [Bruges], where the King was, and demand audience of him. Let but the King hear my Welsh voice outside his door, and he would admit me, no matter who attempted to bar my way. And I felt assured that, could I but speak with him, he would relent and grant me my rights. But, were I denied access, I would take Jacky into France (where the King may not go by reason of the treaty with brute Cromwell), and live quiet there where my enemies could not molest me.

Not wishing to repay my Lord Castlehaven's kindness with ingratitude, I informed him secretly of this project, but he advised me against it, for he said no good would come of it, and that, as I must submit to the King's will at last, I had better do it sooner; for, said he, I would receive no sustenance from the King or from anyone else did I defy him.

To which I replied that I had been given to understand (for I had no experience in the matter) that a well-favoured woman need never lack for bread were she not nice about how 'twas gotten, no, nor for jewels neither; and that, could I not support myself and my son in an honest way, then I must needs become what my enemies falsely swore I was, for I would anything rather than give up the boy.

The which was sinful of me, I own; and I repent that ever I entertained such thought; but so persecuted and distracted and angry was I, that I knew not where to turn nor what to do.

But my Lord Castlehaven was not forward for that plan, neither; he said 'twas madness to think on't, and he laboured to dissuade me from such folly; and for his patience and sympathy I was much beholden to him. For when he perceived that I was resolved to escape from the vicinity of the Court, so that I could negotiate with the King without duress, he said that he would aid me to leave Brussels, provided I did not acquaint him with my place of refuge and he would not be obligated to lie to the King and say he knew not where I was. And so he helped me, as I shall tell.

But while this plan was a-cooking, I writ a letter to the King, and I told him, what he knew well enough, that he had taken an honest, loyal, innocent and loving maid, and he had sullied her by a trick, and made an whore of her, and planted bastards on her, and then cast her aside and set his servants to abuse her, so that all the world pointed the finger of scorn at her and named her an abandoned woman. And she was in truth an abandoned woman, for she had been abandoned by the man she had trusted and loved—and still loved, though she did not trust him any more. And, since 'twas only her desire to do his will, and since he would not support her, it must be his will that she should earn the wherewithal for her necessary expenses by the exercise of the trade he had taught her. And so she would, for it mattered no more to her what her fate was; since she loved him and him alone, and he had abandoned her; and she hoped the next woman he lay with gave him the pox and be damned to him.

That was the sense of the naughty letter I writ to the King in my anger and despair; but I do not think that my Lord Castlehaven despatched it, and perhaps he was wise to rip it up, for 'twas wicked and foolish of me to write so, and I would not have done it, only I was grieved and distracted because the King would take my child away from me.

And that (said Mistress Barlow) is the story of my unhappy

life at Brussels after that I returned from London, when the King abandoned me and his creatures persecuted me. 'Tis the true story, as I hope to be saved; and I tell it as a warning to other trusting maidens, who are minded to surrender their virtue to the lies and promises of a seducing man.

XI Flanders: Battle   (January 1658)

So, COME THE morning (said Mistress Barlow), two of my Lord
Castlehaven's men escorted Jacky and me to a coach bound for
Calais, where we found two places inside, having for companions
an ancient Frenchie and his wife who were both so deaf that
there was no conversation possible, for which I was thankful.
We toiled for three dreary days through the snow, and on the
third night, when we had hoped to have gotten to Calais, we
had perforce to lie at a wretched inn at some spot whose name
I have forgot and have no wish to remember, for 'twas there
that my enemies did me another wrong.

For that night, as I am in my first sleep in a rickety trundle-
bed without curtains, with Jacky slumbering childlike and deep
at my side, I am awakened sudden by a noise, and I perceive
in the moonlight that there are men in the room, and that they
have masks on their faces; and before I can cry out, one of 'em
claps across my mouth a dirty hand smelling of horse-sweat,
and nigh stifles me. And then two of 'em pull me out of the
bed, all in my shift, and I think they purpose me a mischief,
but they do not—for they truss me to a chair, and wind a greasy
scarf round my mouth, so that I can neither move nor cry out;
and then two of 'em carry Jacky away, still sleeping and wrapped
in a blanket, the while I look on helpless; and then t'other two
turn out my travelling trunk and rummage in my garments until
they find the King's letters, which one of the rascals pockets.

So I know they come from the King, for they steal nought but the letters and Jacky's clothes.

Then they take me out from the chair and look carefully to my bonds, and lay me back in the bed and cover me up, so that, although I am nigh distracted, I am at least warm that cold night. And thus they leave me, the villains, with my feet and legs tied together, and my hands bound behind my back, and my arms to my sides, and the noisome scarf over my mouth, till I feel like to suffocate.

All the four scoundrels wear black masks, and black cloaks; and they say nought; so they have planned the business mighty careful; and no doubt they think I shall not recognise 'em, but I am sure the one who led was Prodgers, for he had the build and height of Prodgers, and his breath stank like Prodgers', and he wore a ring the like of one I had seen on Prodgers' finger.

In the morning, when the serving-maid came and found me bound and released me, there was no trace of the men, for snow had fallen in the night and covered their tracks. The landlord and all the people in the inn swore they had heard nought in the night, and I thought that, either they had been bribed to hear nought (the which I believe to be the case), or else they sleep mighty sound natural; for after the villains had left me, and I lay vainly struggling in my bonds, I heard the jingle of bridles and the neighing and tossing of horses, and then horse-hoofs thudding on the hard snow.

And I felt that they took with them all I had to live for.

One thing the leader of the scoundrels did that made me sure he was Prodgers, or at least that he came for the King, and that was, that he put something under the pillow after they laid me back in the bed; and in the morning I found that 'twas a purse, and a purse with gold in it, too. No common robber ever left a purse of gold in place of what he took away, and, though 'twas an insult to give me money in exchange for my son, yet 'twas so unusual a form of insult from my husband that 'twas evident he placed great store on Jacky.

And another thing that showed the King's hand in the cruel

business was, that the scoundrels, though they bound me tight, so that I could not escape nor cry out neither, yet they used me as gently as they might, and they did not assault my modesty, as well they could have. For though tongues wag that I am wanton, yet no servant of the King has ever durst for his life to attempt to ravish me.

I was so prostrated with grief that I could not determine what to do, but the innkeeper and the coachman decided for me, for no doubt they were afeared that their part in the business (viz, sleeping sound and hearing nought) might come out to their hurt; so the landlord's wife packed my trunk for me, and the landlord handed me into the coach, and so I found myself bound for Calais will I nill I, and where for else I neither knew nor cared.

But we had not travelled much above a mile or two, I think, when the coach stopped, and the coachman got down and went to the roadside, and then came and opened the door and bade me urgent to alight; which I did, and there under the bare sticks of the hedge I saw my Jacky—dead, I thought at first, but as soon as I took him in my arms I perceived he was but sleeping, and most peaceful, too.

'Twas the colour of his coat on the ground which had caught the coachman's eye, for all else was white snow, and he remembered the coat and the cut of it, but was afeared to call me until he was satisfied the babe lived.

So overjoyed was I to recover my Jacky, that I all but swooned away, and when I came to myself, and had taken him in my lap in the coach to warm his little body (for he was mighty cold), I bathed him in my joyful tears and could not listen to his story.

But at the last he made me to listen, and a wonderful story 'twas, too. 'Tis not certain that a nine-year-old babe tells the truth exactly, nor remembers exactly, neither; but I heard him relate his adventures many times, and it did not vary much, and there was corroboration from Prodgers too. So this was very like the way of it:

Jacky woke as he found himself carried out of the inn into

the cold air of the night, but ere he could cry out the man who had him in his arms put a hand over his mouth and bade him be quiet; the which puzzled him a little; and they took him across a field and gave him his clothes to put on, and told him he was being taken to the King, and that cheered him.

He was not affrighted, he said, but he was mighty puzzled to find himself in the clutches of strange men when he had fallen asleep in bed with his mother; and he asked where his mother was, and he was told he was not to trouble himself about her because she was warm in bed and she knew he was being taken to the King, because the King would provide for him. He was disinclined to believe these men, but he could do nought else but accept what they told him, and he was mighty cheered when Prodgers came and told him he was to ride on horseback at night through the snow. Prodgers made big with it as an exciting adventure, and one his mother and the King had planned for him; and though he did not believe that his mother would allow him to go without warning him to ride careful, yet he agreed private to himself that 'twould be an entrancing adventure.

Now he was wide awake, and he enjoyed cantering through the snow, but after an hour or more the moon went in and 'twas in darkness they crossed the bridge over an ice-bound river, and began to follow the road on the further bank. Hereabouts, one of the horses cast a shoe, and went lame sudden, and threw its rider, who was a clumsy fellow and who lay stunned on the ground. The others drew rein, and one of 'em alighted to tend the injured man.

Jacky owned as if he wanted to relieve nature, and while he was thus occupied behind the hedge, he heard Prodgers tell one of the men to have a care lest the boy escape, and to tie his hands should he seem to have a mind to.

Such did not appear to Jacky the proper way to guard the son of the King, who was being given a special pleasure by his father, and he began to think he had been abducted by desperate villains who would hold him for ransom from the King; so, being a proper boy and bold and gallant, and not wanting in resource neither, he resolved to fight the three remaining men single-handed, and escape.

So he provided himself with a sharp stick that was lying by the hedge, and, coming up to the men in an easy, innocent sort of fashion, he poked the stick into the flank of the mare he had observed to be the most restless, with the result that the mare reared sudden, and threw her rider, who landed atop the one who had fallen first and was now recovering; and Jacky then whacked the rump of the riderless horse, so that it took to its heels, and the other horses galloped away with it; and the man still a-horse, trying to rein in and dismount simultaneous, fell under his horse and received a kick which was no more, but a good deal less, than he deserved.

When he poked and whacked at the horses, Jacky had gotten himself on the far side of 'em from the group round the man on the ground, so that the horses were away afore Prodgers and the other rogues knew what was a-happening. But when the horses galloped off, the two men still on their feet made a dash at Jacky, but he flung the stick at the legs of the foremost one so that he tripped and went rump over pate, and t'other landed atop of him with a mighty thud and an oath which I have told Jacky he must disremember and never repeat when he tells the story.

So my brave little Jacky, having downed all his enemies and put their horses to flight, then jumped down on to the ice of the river and ran nimbly across to the other side.

When he came to this part of the story, my heart sank, for had not the ice been firm he had been drownded; but he was only a small boy, and, praise be to God, it held his weight.

But it did not hold for Prodgers and his scoundrels, who picked themselves up and jumped on to the ice after Jacky; for he heard it crack and splinter, and then he heard them a-shouting and a-screaming as they plunged down into the icy water. They all four had gotten themselves a ducking and a freezing, and sure it served the villains right enough, and I was mighty glad to hear it, and had they all been drownded I had been glad, but they were not, and lived to tell lies about the business, too.

But my young hero waited not to discover whether they scrambled out or not, and in any case 'twas too dark to see; he was afeared he would be catched if they came up to him, so he ran as fast as his little legs could carry him in the direction of the inn where he had left his mother. But he missed his way somewheres (and 'twas God's mercy he did, for he would not have gotten on to the Calais road else), and the journey was too far; and at last he was so tired his little legs could carry him no more, so he sat down under a hedge to await the morning, and so fell asleep, and there we found him, thanks be to God, for had not the coachman noticed the colour of his coat, he had been froze to death.

And that (said Mistress Barlow) is the story of how the King stole my babe Jacky from me and of how the boy confounded his captors and escaped. It is the true story, so far as I have been able to piece it together from what I have been told.

XII Calais: Final Surrender

(January 1658)

I WAS MIGHTY puzzled to know what to do next (said Mistress Barlow), for I was resolved not to give up my son, yet I saw now that the King would stick at nothing to have him; so we would not be safe this side the sea. So my first resolve was to take ship to England and (with the aid of the gold Prodgers had left with me) make my way with all secrecy and expedition to County Pembroke at the far end of Wales, where perhaps I might find some kind fellow-countryman who would marry a King's abandoned mistris without a dowry, and have a care for her children. For though I loved the King still, I realised he loved me no longer, and 'twould not be treason to marry.

But at Calais all the talk was that there were no ships for England, by reason of the intense cold, so I took lodging in a quiet street, and then made my way to an inn at the other end of the town, and enquired if they would, for a consideration, send letters for me and retain answers until I called for 'em. The which they agreed to do.

The first letter I writ was to my Lord Castlehaven, who I told about my son being stolen from me, and that I was distraught, and that all my papers had been stolen, too (but not that Jacky was safe with me again), and I prayed him to ask the King to let me know, in mercy's sake, what he had done with my son.

And after some days I had an answer from my Lord Castle-haven, that he was mighty sorry to hear my news, and that he was taking coach himself to see the King and to lay my case afore him; and that what he regretted about the whole tragical business was that it had been one of his own men that had been bribed by Dan O'Neile to tell by which coach I had left town; and so the kidnappers had tracked me. And he said he had dismissed the man.

When I went to the inn next day to enquire for letters, there I found my Lord Castlehaven's footman, mighty tired and foot-sore, for he had walked all the way from Brussels, almost, to beg my pardon and to entreat with me that he had given the information only because he was told that 'twas for the King and he needed the money for his wife, who was to be brought to bed and had no warm covering nor kindling for a fire this cold winter; and he had promised that if I would write a letter to my Lord and ask him to give him his post again, he would tell me where they had taken my son.

And so mighty curious was I to learn more about the business that I writ the letter he pled for, and so he told me that Dan O'Neile had told him that the King's son was to be put to school at Paris. He knew not the names of any of the men who were with Prodgers, for 'twas Dan O'Neile he had had to do with.

When I went to the inn the next day, I was told there was a fine gentleman to see me, and that he was in the best room, and I was to go up to him. So I went up to the best room, expecting, maybe, that my fine visitor would be my Lord Castle-haven, or my Lord Taafe, or perhaps Subtle Dan O'Neile, or even pimp Prodgers arrayed to appear like a gentleman. But 'twas none of these.

'Twas the King himself.

And when I saw 'twas the King, I curtsied low, and was silent, for I could think of nought to say to this tall, dark man who I loved so much and who had treated me so cruel.

He came with rapid strides to me, and took me by the

shoulders, and made to kiss me, but I put my head down, and denied him the freedom of my lips.

And when he reproved me gently that I would not accord him even a kiss, I asked him why he expected that I should desire him to kiss me, since he had used me so shameful; but he did not answer that, but handed me to a chair, and bade me to sit so that we could converse together.

The lines about his mouth were deeper than I remembered them, and his eyes were sad. 'Twas nearly two years since last I saw him, and he looked infinite older than by two years, and worn and unhappy; and my heart struggled to melt to him. But I would not obey him. I remained standing by the chair, and curtsied again, and said (pert, no doubt) that I thanked His Majesty, but I considered that such as I must stand in the Royal Presence.

He did not press his request, but turned away, and said, half over his shoulder, that we should not quarrel, for he had grievous news for me.

To that I said nought, and he went over to the window, and looked out, saying that the villains who had abducted our son had been captured and had confessed; and had he the power he had had them hanged.

To which I said that so would I, but for the fact that, were they hanged, their master that sent them should be hanged too.

His reply, still gazing out of the window, was that he wished he knew who their master was, for they were scoundrels; and I said I wondered he should say that for they were indeed scoundrels, and he knew who their master was as well as I did.

And when he again denied gravely that he knew who their master was, I lost all patience with the man, and told him saucy to tell that to his aunt Eliza; and when he looked round astonished, I stammered out that I had quite forgot that he had an aunt Eliza [Queen Elizabeth of Bohemia], but that, even so, I was assured she would believe him more than I did; for I knew that one of the villains was prying Prodgers, for I recognised the ring on his finger, and the stink of his breath, too, and no one but prying Prodgers' master would leave me a purse of gold in exchange for my son; and I said, moreover, that, had I only known that I was to be meeting the scoundrels' master to-day, I had brought the purse with me and flung it in his face—only I would keep the gold because I had need of it.

The King gave over his lying then, and acknowledged straight that, though he had neither planned the expedition nor known it had set out, yet those who planned it were acting on his intention that he was resolved to have the boy. He owned he was mighty sorry I had suffered rough handling, for he had given strict instructions always that I was to be treated gentle, and not to be offered insult or injury; and he said, too, that, as for the gold, I was right welcome to it.

He said all this sincere, and I think he so intended it, yet his mind was not on his words, and his looks were so mournful and uneasy that I was minded to forgive him all the wrong he had done me, but I hardened my heart and I looked him stern in the face and demanded to be told where my boy was; and I did not blush when I asked him, neither.

He would not look at me then, but turned away again, and hesitated, and was so ill-at-ease that I all but ran to him and kissed him to give him comfort; but I waited, and at last he said that, Faith! he wished he knew where the boy was.

And when I enquired of him why he did not know, seeing 'twas he who stole the babe from me, he all of a sudden flung his hat off, and put his arm on the table, and his head on it, and fell a-weeping.

I stood there silent, and watched this tall brute sobbing as though his heart had broken, and I perceived that, though he loved me no longer, yet he loved my son; and then nought could prevent my weeping, too; so I ran to him and put my arm round him and caressed him, and he drew me towards him, not as a masterful man takes hold of a submissive maid, but as an unhappy boy clings to his mother; and so we sat there for a quarter of an hour or more, like two fountains playing over each other; and between his sobs he confessed that the boy he doted on was dead, that he had run from his abductors when they halted by the river, and he had jumped on to the ice and it had given way and he had fallen in and been carried away by the current and drownded.

So then I was sitting on his knee as of old, and we were kissing each other's tears away, and I perceived that nothing would ever prevent my loving this man as long as I lived, or submitting to whatever his will for me might be; yet I could not resist the temptation to play with him and to tease him a while longer, and to make him suffer for his unkindness, so I asked him to tell me his plans for the boy, had he lived until his father reigned royal in Whitehall; and, indeed, when he told me, they were so generous and so splendid that I marvelled, for though he did not say so in words precise that he intended to make Jacky his legitimate heir, yet he implied it.

And even in that moment of thanksgiving and joy there was wickedness and unforgiving hate in my heart, for not only was I proud for myself and gratified for my babe, but I was glad that the Duke of York should be pushed out of the line of succession.

I asked the King to tell me exact what had happened when Jacky had escaped, and he told me that Prodgers had said that, when a horse cast a shoe and the party came to a halt, Jacky had asked permission to relieve himself, and instead of doing so had ran straight on to the ice, which had cracked under him, and he had gone under at once, and though all four men had jumped into the water to rescue him, they had not found his body, and so had concluded he had been swept away by the current and drownded.

When he had done, and was weeping again at the telling of it, I told him that prying Prodgers was a confounded liar, but 'twas not to be wondered at, seeing who his master was. ('Twas on his master's knee I was perched when I said it.) And I told him that the truth was that his son had attacked three grown men with nought but a stick, and had put their horses to flight, and stretched all the men full length on the ground, and then had

run across the river on the ice, whiles those who tried to chase
after him fell through and were all wetted and froze.

Wonder grew in the King's face as he listened, and when he
asked how I knew the story in so particular and in such detail,
I said I knew it in my bones, for Jacky was the King's son and
was not born to be drownded.

At which he demanded was I sure the boy was alive; and
when I owned he had been alive an hour ago, he said that then
I must know where he was, and where the devil was he?

To which I replied that I knew where he was an hour ago,
but belike prying Prodgers had stolen him away since, for I
now perceived that the King had come to Calais to cozen me
whiles his villains stole my babe again.

The King began to protest, upon his honour, that I wronged
him and that he had no such intention, nor no such thoughts,
neither; but I told him, playfully enough, for I was still sitting
on his lap, and he had one arm round my waist and another
under my knees, etc., that 'twere best he did not mention his
honour to me, for I knew what a King's honour was worth.

So then he requested me most humble, as a father and not
as a King, that I should lead him to where the boy was, so that
he might see him with his own eyes and satisfy himself that
he lived and was well, for there was nothing in the whole world
he loved and valued more than my Jacky; and because I believed
that this was so (though I believed nought else the King said
to me), I led him to my lodging, where Jacky was, and such
was the King's delight at seeing the boy again after he had
thought him drownded, and at hearing from his own lips the
story of how he had defeated four grown men and given them a
fall each and a ducking, and such was the boy's delight at seeing his father again, and at being able to boast and brag to
him of how he had fought his first battle, and beat in it, that
I had not the heart to deny either of them anything.

And such an afternoon 'twas, too, and such a clacking of
tongues, that there never will be the like of it in Calais again;
for what with the King relating for the thousandth time the

narration of his escape after Worcester fight, and Jacky relating
for the hundredth time the story of his escape after the tussle
at the river, I was minded to knock their heads together (only
I durst not strike the King, for 'tis High Treason to do so), and
remind them that they were not the only ones present who had
come through adventures and perils and 'scaped from 'em.

But so happy was I to see the two of 'em so happy together,
and yet sad to think that I must give up my babe, that I knew
not whether to laugh or cry. And as I sat there and watched
these two male folk I loved so much, and harkened to their
stories that I knew so well, I debated within myself whether I
should plead with the King again to have me at Court with
him, as his mistris, or his kitchen-maid, or as serving-maid to
his wife when he has gotten himself one, or in any capacity
whatsoever, or whether I had best retire from my ambitions
and so live my life out quiet, in the solace of my memories
of the King's one-time love for me, and of my pride in my
son. And I resolved, as I reflected on the ten years since I crossed
seas to France and became the King's mistris, that all my miseries
and troubles arose because of the fact that I had been sinful and
had surrendered to my love for him; so I resolved, with God's
help, to sin no more, and to resist such overtures as the King
might make to me that we should resume our former way of
life together, even if 'twere but for the once.

But it almost broke my heart to resolve so, for though 'tis
not difficult for a maid to vow to be chaste when the man she
loves in vain is far away, and she has no occasion to be otherwise, yet 'tis hard to make such a resolution (and harder still
to adhere to it) when that same man is in the house alone with
her, and displays intention to remain for the night.

But such was the resolution I made, and I was proud and
conceited of myself that I could make it; and when I had put
Jacky to his bed (for this babble-babble-babble had wearied him
early) I told the King that he had best seek him a bed at the
inn, for I was resolved to abjure fornication and all unchastity,
and to live continent for the rest of my life.

To which he replied that 'twas indeed a noble resolution, and he admired and honoured me for it, and he wished to God he had the strength of will to do likewise, but he was much afeared he had not.

To which I said that 'twould be a waste of breath and time for him to make such a resolve, for I was convinced he would not give over wenching whiles breath was in his body; and he conceded with a sigh that no doubt I had the rights of it, for there was no pleasure in life he valued more and nothing gave him more satisfaction. And I said, Shame on him! for he knew right well that fornication was a sin; and I went on to reproach him for his evil way of living, and the great noise he made in the world turning chaste virgins into whores; but he protested that such stories were much exaggerated, and moreover that to hear me preach a sermon on chastity was like hearing the Duke of Bucks denounce duelling. And when I asked him what the devil he meant by that, he said that no doubt he had heard as many tales to the detriment of my reputation as I had heard of his, and when I challenged him to name one such story, he said that Tom Howard swore he had gotten the pox by me, and I said that that was a filthy lie, for though I thought it likely that Tom Howard had the pox, yet he had not gotten it from me, for I never had to do with him in my life, nor had I never had the pox neither, for I had given the right of my body to but one man, and that man the King, as he very well knew.

But the King said he did not see how he could be expected to bear witness to that, for he was not Groom of my Bedchamber; and I said that 'twas shame on him he were not, for he alone had the key to it, and, if he were, he would know that when he was away from it, my bed was chaste, which was the devil a sight more than the Groom of his Bedchamber could say about His Majesty's bed.

He said grave that he hoped indeed I spake truth, for indeed the stories about me were many and various, and some most particular. And I said they was all lies, spread by men who had desired to have me, and who I had refused, and boxed their

ears for it, as I had boxed the ears of the Duke of York when
he had made insinuations and suggestions to me; and I said that
the stories about him were many and various too, and in particular
there was his planting a bastard on Mistress Pegge, which had
brought her to bed at such a time that he must have had his
sinful pleasure of her body the same month as I was walled up
in the Tower of London in misery and danger of the torture for
his sake.

He said, Faith! he did not see that it would have had me out
of the Tower sooner had he turned monk whiles I was in there,
and indeed, when he lay with Mistress Pegge, 'twas a tribute
to me, for he never lay with a wench but he thought of me, and,
sure, he hoped 'twas the same with me and that I always thought
of him likewise.

To which I replied that 'twas indeed the case that I never lay
with a man but I thought of His Majesty, for I never in my
life lay with any man save His Majesty, no, nor never desired
to, neither. And I added, too, that when I thought, as often I
did, that I had given all to such a whoreson seducer as he was,
I was sick with shame, and I verily believed that there had never
been a King of England, no, nor of France, Scotland, Ireland or
Wales, neither, no, nor in the whole world from Muscovy to
far Cathay, who had brought so many innocent virgins to misery
and wretchedness as he had, and that when his name was added
to the scroll of the Kings of England, 'twould not be as Charles
the Good or Charles the Bold, or Charles the Great, or Charles
the Wise, nor even as Charles the Tall, or Charles the Black Boy,
neither; but as Charles the Seducer.

But he said, no, he thought not; he thought it more like he
would be called, Charles, the Father of his People.

And when I cried, Shame! on him, he but laughed and said
that, Faith! 'twas hard that a King who had been denied his
throne and his estates and his palaces, and was obliged to subsist
on charity, and spend his days in plots and schemes, should not
have the comfort of a brisk wench in his bed o'nights when the
desire came on him.

To which I said that he had no need to remind me that 'twas a hard world, for I knew that better than he did, and 'twas his fault the world was so hard for me. But he said that he did not see why he should be expected to bear all the blame for my misfortunes, for, as he remembered the occasion, when we first come together, I was as eager for it as he was, if not more so.

And so incensed was I at this insult (though 'twas true, too) that I slapped his face with all my might.

He drew back startled, for he had not expected that I would hit him; and I drew back, too, for I was dismayed, for 'tis High Treason to strike the King.

So we stared at each other for the space of a minute or more, and I was afeared for what he should do to me, since I had never hit him afore, nor he me, save only in sport, and he is a strong man who does not control his strength when governed by passion, as well I knew, and he had me at his mercy, for we were alone in the house; and as I stared at him, fearful, and shrank back, for I thought he would beat me,—I loved the man so, for he looked so tall and kingly, that I knew that if he beat me to the death I should die happy, for 'twas my destiny to love and to submit myself to him and to be used by him in whatever way he pleased.

For a minute or more we stared each other out of countenance, and then my eyes dropped, for I could not outface him, and I stood there, trembling, awaiting his pleasure.

Maybe he discerned the fear in my eyes, or the love in 'em, for he laughed, and put his hand to his cheek, and rubbed the red patch which showed where I had slapped him, and said, all rueful, that, Faith! he was damned if 'twas no more than his deserts, and if 'twould give me satisfaction, why, I could box t'other ear likewise. But I burst into tears and fell on my knees and took his hands and kissed 'em, and begged forgiveness for my ingratitude and ill temper.

He would not suffer me to kneel to him, but set me on my feet again, and kissed me, and bade me kiss the place where I had cuffed him, and vowed that 'twas for me to forgive him and not t'other way round, for when I wept at him, he could deny me nought, and 'twas plaguey hard on his conscience to keep making promises that he would not keep and did not intend to keep, neither.

To which I replied, through my tears and smiles, that I knew that 'twas I who was to blame for my misfortunes, but I could not help myself, for I loved him, and that I knew I had no right to be envious of the other mistrises he took, nor to reproach him with 'em neither, for 'twas his right and privilege and duty as King to take his pleasure and his recreation where he willed, and no man should deny him, nor no woman neither; yet I could not prevent my envy, for I was assured no other wench could love him as I did, and all my desire was to be with him, and to have some share of his attention, which was only right as I was his first love and the mother of his first-born children, and that I was sure I could satisfy him as much as any wench he could find in the whole wide world, for I was still young and brisk and loving, and as fit for a king's embraces as ever I had been.

And so, afore I knew what was happening and could prevent him, all my good resolutions were in the fire, and I was naked in his arms again, and half laughing and half weeping as he whispered to me that really he was a great fool and deserved to have his ears boxed for it, to seek out other women, but, Faith! he only did it out of curiosity, to discover could there be another wench in the world so sweet and loving as Lucy Barlow, and now he was convinced there was not; but, indeed, lying with a wench was an absurd and unconscionably ridiculous pastime, and undignified, too, for a King, and there was no profit in it. After a while, he said that he had had his fill of fornication, and when he came into his kingdoms he would give it over entirely, and occupy himself on Affairs of State, and doing good to his people and governing of 'em well, so they could live easy in their minds and get children without fear for their futures, had they a mind to such philoprogenitive antics. And after another pause, he said that he would not give it over

absolute, for he would marry me and have me for his bed-mate
sole, and his Queen, too, and my Jacky should be Prince of
Wales, and reign after him, and get a Prince of Wales and a
King in his turn, too, he hoped.

But I told him to keep his big ugly mouth shut and enjoy
himself whiles the occasion offered, for if he preached like that
to the next trollop he copulated with, she'd bite his tongue off.

And so we lay there with great satisfaction to the two of us,
but I did not believe a word of what he was saying.

I was justified, too, for in the morning, when he was dressed,
and all his passion spent, I pleaded with him to have me at
Court with him, so that I could be acknowledged and freed
from men's insults, and all he said was, that he would think on
it. And when I pressed him, not to think on't, but to act on't,
he laughed and said that, could I but control my fierce temper
and keep always a firm grip on my sharp tongue and my ten-
stun right hand, why, then, I could be more acceptable at Court,
but, Faith! even a king did not fancy having his face slapped
too often, howsoever he might deserve it.

And when I protested that I had never hit him but the once,
and never would do it again, he said that the first time he ever
saw me I was boxing a man's ears, and the first thing I ever
said to him was that I would never box his, and now I had boxed
his ears, just as I had boxed his brother's, and, from all he heard,
my path through life was adorned by men rubbing their boxed
ears, and though boxing ears might be my pleasure, why, to
have his ears boxed was not his; and, further, that did he have
me at Court, he doubted not that the whole place would resound
with slaps from dewy morn till sleepy bedtime, and maybe after
that, so that 'twould be like living perpetual in the midst of a
company of musqueteers repelling attack.

And all this because I slapped him impulsive once when he
insulted me!

So I said I was mighty glad he was able to be so merry at
my expense, and that I would be at his service all my life,
whether to be mocked at or for any other purpose, even to the

slapping of his cheeks when he needed it. But the latter offer he saw fit to decline, saying that he wanted his ears boxed so often (the which I could well believe) that 'twould wear out my right hand, and his cheeks, too, did he retain me at Court as the Royal Ear-Boxer; and that I must clearly understand that, when he sent for me, as he intended to do, 'twould not be for that purpose, but for a quite other purpose, and I must not come unless on that understanding.

To which I replied that nothing in the whole world could please me better, and he could not send for me too soon for my liking, for I was always at his service and his service alone, and was proud to be his Lady of Pleasure, and always would be. But that was more than a half of a year since, and he has not sent for me, and I do not think he will send for me, for there are those about him that are my enemies, and have persuaded him that he cannot gain the approbation of his peoples and so recover his crown whiles I am at his side, and in particular the Duke of York is my enemy, for reasons which I have explained before. . . .

Ere he left Calais, I came to an agreement with the King to surrender my son, for I saw there was no remedy, and Jacky desired it too, for his father tempted him with promises of his having a horse and a sword and a manservant of his own. And though I know full well what the King's promises are worth, Jacky did not, and believed 'em. So I allowed that Jacky should be put under the care of Mr Crofts [later Lord Crofts], who was to be his guardian, and to teach him all things being necessary to a gentleman, and a King's son.

The King said I must write to Mr Mottet and tell him I would allow my son to be dealt with at the King's pleasure, for so the Spanish would believe they had done the business and not the King himself, and they would be more disposed to aid the King to recover his crown; for, said the King, 'tis in human nature that we feel benevolent towards those we have done favours to, and resentment towards those who do favours to us. So I writ as he commanded.

But my troubles were not over then, not by no means. For I stipulated that before I should give up my son his father would settle on me a regular and certain sum of money, so that I should live with dignity and respect, as became the mother of the King's children, and perhaps have his daughter Mary to live with me again. For my pension was no more nor words in brute Cromwell's printed sheets. And the King promised me faithful that he would prevail with Chancellor Hyde to make arrangements to pay my pension regular, and the arrearages as well. But either he forgot or Chancellor Hyde found other purposes for his money, and as for my arrearages, I knew I could whistle for 'em for all the hope I had of getting 'em.

And the King cozened me in the end, or at least my backside friends around him did; for I put Jacky to lodge with an English schoolmaster to learn his book and fit him for schooling; and when I went to visit him one day, the babe was gone and the schoolmaster owned he did not know where he was. Or he had pocketed a shut-mouth bribe, likely. All he would say was that that base lying fellow Tom Ross had come and said 'twas the King's order he should be removed hence.

I knew 'twas useless to complain to the King, for I am confident that, when he is away from me, he does not concern himself whether I laugh or weep; so I put my case to the Burgomaster, that the King's son was kidnapped by villains who would hold him for ransom; and after ten or a dozen days they found where my Jacky was.

So then I writ to the King and demanded he should keep his promise to me, and Harry Bennet writ back that 'twas all a misunderstanding, and that the King had told Master Ross he would not have me abused, but that the boy was to be put to school in Paris; and the King allowed I should reside at Paris to be near my son and to have access to him.

But all that was in the future on that morning in Calais which was the last occasion I have seen my King and husband and master. Then he was all loving and I all compliant, and I felt like a true wife whose husband leaves her but for a journey, and soon they will be in each other's arms again. But I did not ask the King for my papers back, for I knew that, did I ask for them, he would swear mighty that he had not got them and had never had them and if prying Prodgers had stolen them 'twas not by his orders; and belike they have been destroyed, for though they did not prove my marriage, yet they contained divers promises from the King which implied it. And I thought, too, that, did I press the matter, he had essayed to persuade me that I had never received any letters or papers from him, and had he attempted such, I had lost my temper and slapped his face again. And I think that 'tis better to suffer silent than be reputed a termagant. So I kissed his unslapped cheek and he went away.

And now I live on from day to day, vowing to myself that I wish never to see my Black Boy again, not ever, and yet hoping with all my heart that he will send for me to go to him; and so I suppose I shall endure until it shall please God to restore him in triumph to his kingdom, though when that shall be we can only trust Almighty God to reveal in His own good time; and what my fate shall be when my husband is King indeed, I do not know, and can only await in doubt and dismay.

And that (said Mistress Barlow) is the story of my sad life, as I have lived it up to this second day of August in the year fifty-eight. 'Tis a story of the misery and wretchedness that have accompanied me along the path of sin; and if it has a moral in it for other wenches (aye, and for men, too), then I am happy to be held up to succeeding generations as an example that those who are tempted from innocent and chaste ways should consider before they depart from 'em, for though I have gotten some days and hours of ecstasy and great joy in my marriage, yet for the most part my reward has been shame and despair, and that though I have loved but one man only, and remained faithful to him always. That is the truth, before Almighty God, as I hope to be saved; for I am sincerely a penitent, and I rely on His Mercy and Justice towards a poor, unfortunate sinner. I trust that I shall not appeal to Him in vain.

Postscript

(Presumably drafted by Dean Cosin or by his clerk, the amanuensis.)

THE FOREGOING NARRATIVE of her sad life was told to Dean Cosin by Mistress Lucy Barlow (as she called herself) at divers interviews during the summer of 1658 at the Dean's house at Paris. Having lived a thoughtless and sinful life for upwards of ten years as the mistris of the King, she was now a sorrowful penitent, and she applied to the Dean for advice and instruction in the consolations of true religion. At his suggestion, Mistress Barlow related her life story with the intent that his clerk should write it out from her own lips as a warning to other maids who might be tempted to stray from the paths of virtue, stipulating only that it might not be made public during the lifetime of his Sacred and Gracious Majesty, King Charles the Second.

But little remains to be added to her narrative. In the August of '58, Mistress Barlow journeyed to Brussels with intent to interview the King, but she returned saying it had been a sleeveless errand and she had been cozened. The King had departed elsewhere, and the only member of his family she could find was his chaplain, Dr Lloyd, who declined to reveal to her where the King was or to receive a message for him.

So downcast was Mistress Barlow by the failure of her mission that she owned that her desire to continue living was but slight, and when she fell sick of the small-pox, she was content to slip from this sinful and malicious world.

Mistress Lucy Walter or Barlow died on the third day of October, in the year of Our Lord sixteen hundred and fifty eight. Had she lived, the Dean believed, she had passed the rest of her life as a virtuous and honest woman. By the Grace of God, Dr Cosin was with her to the end, and she passed to eternal life in complete penitence and in the full belief of the blessed love and mercy of Almighty God and the sure hope of a joyful resurrection.

Through the kind offices of William Erskine, Esq., Cup-Bearer to His Majesty, and at that time resident in Paris, her mortal remains were interred in the Huguenot Cemetery, but by some oversight her grave was not marked by a stone.

May her bones rest in peace.

In accordance with her final wish, these papers have been bound up and deposited in safe keeping pending the melancholy event on which they may be published to all the world.

[The following, in the handwriting of the amanuensis, was on a loose slip of paper at the end of the book] :

The Lady Lucy Barlow was a most beauteous Lady and of a most vivacious and engaging Manner; though far past her Prime, being upwards of nearly thirty Years of Age, she had retained both her Looks and the Spriteliness of her Bearing. Her Hair was Lustrous, and Golden Brown in Colour. She spoke in the Welsh Manner, as if she were Singing, and her Voice was Low and Sweet. She spoke, too, with Passion, and very Fast, sometimes with Laughter, and oft-times with Tears. I, who was accorded the Privilege of sitting Day by Day with the Lady Lucy and the Dean, to the intent that I might write in Shorthand the Words which poured from her Lips, am an old Man and a poor, and had I not learned in Youth the Facility to Read and Write and to copy down Speech in Shorthand, I had never seen such Beauty save afar off. The Lady Lucy was of Gentle Birth and of the Blood Royal, though that was Far Removed; yet farther still was I, the Clerk, from the Lady Lucy. The Lady Lucy had been a Sinner, the Mistris of the King; and Beauty is not existing below the Skin. Yet it is Strange, this Beauty, that it should move the shrivelled Heart of the poor Clerk, that though he be not fit to Kiss her Hand, yet he should long to wipe away her Tears.

Appendix: The Historical Basis for the Narrative

I *Wales: The Beginning* (July 1645)

The detailed records of Charles I's weeks in Wales after Naseby do not include a night at Golden Grove; so a meeting there with the Prince of Wales (then in Devonshire) is historically possible only if the diaries were faked to keep the meeting secret. I claim the novelist's licence for this. We don't know where Lucy was; her presence there is not impossible.

II *England: The King's Treasure* (Winter 1647-8)

For the Walter lawsuit, see the House of Lords records summarised in the 4th, 5th and 6th *Reports of the Historical Manuscripts Commission* and the *Journals of the House of Lords, 1641-7*.

There is no documentary evidence of when, by what route and in whose company Lucy went abroad. James II and Clarendon say she sailed direct to Holland; but her son was born in April 1649 and Charles's stay at The Hague in July 1648 was brief and busy; that Lucy went to Paris (and on Royalist business) and accompanied him to Holland, is more likely in view of their continued association and the documents quoted below:

'11 September 1649. To Joseph Butler, Messenger, and the rest of the messengers: To summon Jas. Mosie and Eliz. his wife, Eliz. Cavalier, Orton Brooke, Thos. and Bridget Wells, Margaret Sode, Lucie Walter, and Mathias Nicholls, before Council, to declare as to certain treasure hidden, belonging to the State.' [*Calendar of State Papers, Domestic*, 1649-50, p. 546. Warrants issued by Council of State.]

I have been unable to find any record of arrests under this warrant, but in the Black Box enquiry of 1680 William Disney (who was hanged in 1685 for printing Monmouth's Declaration) said that Margaret Sambourne had told someone else that 'she was putt in prison about her sayd nieces Mrs Barlow going beyond seas'. [*British Museum Add. MSS 28094*, fo. 71]

Royalist correspondence in 1649 discusses pawning the Crown Jewels in terms implying they had reached Paris recently, but without saying who brought them. [*Nicholas Papers*, I, 153-7]

III *France: Ecstasy* (Spring 1648)

No evidence has ever come to light of a marriage between Lucy and Charles, and no reputable historian believes there was such a marriage. In 1679 and 1680 Charles made several solemn official denials of marrying Lucy, and all his actions supported his words. But Lucy had some compromising papers he was anxious to obtain from her in 1657, and a mock marriage is a possibility.

IV *Holland: Illusion* (June 1648-April 1649)

Charles's cousin Sophia records his courtship at this period: 'He and I had always been on the best of terms, as cousins and friends, and he had shown a liking for me with which I was much gratified. One day, however, his friends Lord Gerit [Gerard] and Somerset Fox, being in want of money, persuaded him to pay me compliments on the promenade at Vorhoeit.

Among other things he told me I was handsomer than Mrs
Berlo, and that he hoped soon to see me in England.' Sophia
goes on to say that she was 'highly offended' when she learned
that his object in flattering her was to get money for his friends.
[*Memoirs of Sophia*, pp. 23-4]

Who Was Monmouth's Father? The Memoirs of James II
contain a famous passage to the effect that Monmouth was the
son of Robert Sidney; this was gossip which crops up in some
of the scurrilous poems and pamphlets of the time, and John
Evelyn gives it belief in his diary entry recording Monmouth's
execution. James repeated the story in his Testament to his son,
'The Old Pretender', but not where it would naturally be if
he believed it—in the scores of anxious letters he wrote to his
friends during the years when Monmouth was challenging him
for the succession. In two earlier letters he refers to Monmouth
as his nephew. [*Calendar of State Papers, Domestic, Mar.-Dec.
1678*, p. 358; Dartmouth MSS, pp. 34-5.] The evidence that
everyone in public life (including James's older son, the Duke of
Berwick) believed that Monmouth was Charles's son, is over-
whelming, and few historians now accept the Robert Sidney story.

V *Paris: Doubt*   (May 1649-May 1650)

John Evelyn was in Paris in August 1649, and records in his
diary: 'On the 18 I went to St Germains to kisse his Majesties
hands; In this coach (which was my Lord Willmots), went Mrs
Barlow, the Kings Mistris & mother to the Duke of Monemoth,
a browne, beautifull, bold but insipid creature.' His entry for
15 July 1685 refers to Monmouth's mother as 'a beautifull
strumpet, whom I had often seene at Paris'. [de Beer's 6-volume
edition]

A remark in Carte's *Life of Ormond* [III, 479] that 'a fair
lady' delayed Charles's departure from Paris for 'near three
months' is less likely to refer to Lucy than to La Grande Mademoiselle—who herself may have been referring to Lucy when she
recorded her aunt's drawing her attention to a 'dame anglaise,

dont son fils était amoureux', adding: ' He is very apprehensive lest you should discover it; see, how ashamed he looks at her while you are present; he fears that I shall tell you of it.' [*Memoirs*, Colburn, 1848, I, 134]

In the Black Box enquiry, William Disney said ' that Mrs Sambourne who was aunt to Mrs Barlow' told someone else ' that her niece Mrs Barlow had told her that she was married to the King'. Disney further said that ' one Mr Gosfritt a Dutch merchant who lives in the Citty of London (whose Brother married Mrs Barlow's Aunt as he told this Informant) blaming Mrs Barlow's Mother for leaving her daughter abroad in an ill way of living, said the said Mother to Mrs Barlow reply'd, he was mistaken, for her said daughter was married to the King.' [*British Museum Add. MSS 28094*, fo. 71]

VI *Breda: Disillusion* (July 1650–December 1651)

It would take a long chapter to examine the case for and against Charles II having been the father of Lucy's daughter Mary. The evidence for is at least as strong as the evidence against. She was believed to be the King's daughter in Holland where she was born and lived when young, the King provided for her in childhood and she was a royal pensioner all her life. The article in the *Dictionary of National Biography* on Lucy says that Mary was born on 6 May 1651 (eleven months after Charles sailed for Scotland), but when G. D. Gilbert challenged the author of the article to produce evidence of that date, he said he couldn't remember where he found it, and was too busy to look it up; and though many writers have used the date, none have given any other reference than the *D.N.B.*, and I have been unable to find it in any contemporary document.

One of Mary's putative fathers was Lord Taafe; in October 1654 Lord Hatton told Sir Edward Nicholas of gossip—' scurrilous stuffe of Dan O'Neile and Lady Standhop and Lord Taff and Mrs Barlow '—in terms which suggest he did not believe it. [*Nicholas Papers*, II, 110] O'Neile later married Lady Stanhope.

AW M

Betty Killigrew (wife of Francis Boyle, Viscount Shannon) bore Charles a daughter early in 1651; this girl married James Howard, son of Lucy's cousin, 'Suffolk Tom Howard'. Catherine Pegge bore Charles a son (Charles FitzCharles—'Don Carlos') at Bruges in 1657, and also, some writers say, a daughter.

James II implies that Lucy joined Charles in Paris in 1651, but the passage is muddled. A letter from Hyde (6 August 1652) refers to an unnamed 'lady', to whom Charles gave forty pistoles 'which is all the mony he hath received since he came hither, and in some tyme before'. [Bray's *Evelyn*, 1854 edition, IV, 254]

VII *The Low Countries: Opportunity*
(January 1652-November 1654)

There is no evidence that James gave a thought to Lucy while she was alive; he had many admirable qualities, but he was as sexually eager as his brother, and rivalled him in the number of his mistresses and bastards. He envied his brother; it is not impossible that he tried to seduce his brother's mistress. His Testament to his son includes seven foolscap pages of print on the miseries he had experienced in giving way to sexual excess. [Stanier Clarke, II, 622-31]

In his leisurely journey to Cologne, Charles passed through Liége on 18 or 19 July; suggestions by Monmouth's followers, thirty years later, that he married Lucy there, are not credible, but Lucy was at Liége that summer. Harry Bennet (Arlington—another putative father of Lucy's daughter) wrote to Ormond from Paris on 11/21 August 1654: 'I am very sorry for what you tell me of Mrs Barlow's being come to Liége because I have had the fortune most accidentally to hear it censured severely by persons that honour and love the King. I hope D. O'Neil is not guilty for more than himself therein and should be infinitely sory he should be for so much. . . .' [Historical Manuscripts Commission *Ormond Papers* at Kilkenny Castle, New Series, I, 303]

Sir Henry de Vic (*c.* 1598-1671). James II, according to Macpherson [I. 76] wrote that 'When the King went to Germany, [Lucy] imposed on Sir H. V. the King's resident at Brussels, to go along with her to Cologne, and ask leave to marry him. But all being in vain . . .' No reason is given for all being in vain, and the Queen of Bohemia told Sir Edward Nicholas that it was Sir Henry, not Lucy, who was the wooer:

11/21 December 1654: '. . . I have heard the reason of Sr. Henry de Vics journey to Coloign: since it is a doting time for the Kings oulde Ministers of State, I thanke God your wife is yet alive, for feare you should fall in love again. . . .'

4 January 1655: '. . . I am sorrie for poore Sr. Henry de Vic, for lett the match break or goe on, it is everie way ill for him.' [Bray's *Evelyn*, 1854 edition, IV, 218-9, 221]

Hyde writing to Ormond from Cologne on 19/29 December 1654, refers to Sir H. de Vic (who you know is languishing here in a wise business)'. [Historical Manuscripts Commission, *Ormond Papers*, as above, I, 312]; and one of Thurloe's spies reported from Cologne on 12 January 1655: 'Sir Henry Ducie hath beene here som time, which I forgot to tell you of, where lies a story concerning Mrs Barlo, sed tace. You may knowe more hereafter. Shee is here with her yonge heir. . . .' [*Thurloe State Papers*, III, 100] There the record ends; we don't know what the King said.

VIII *The Hague: Realisation* (November 1654-April 1656)

In 1658 a Royalist named Kingstonn remarked in a private letter that the King 'acquir'd without doubt grace from Heaven, and an advantageous esteem among men' by 'driving out of Cullen a person, who gave his enemies a subject of discours'. [*Thurloe State Papers*, VII, 325] If this 'person' was Lucy she would have had cause to be the mysterious 'sulking wife' referred to by the Princess Royal in three of her letters to Charles.

(The Hague, 9 November 1654) '. . . your mothere say's that the greatest thankfulnes shee can show for the honour of your kind remembrance, is to have a special care of you wife for feare her husband here may make her forget them that are absent, your wife thanks you in her own hand, and still, though she begs me very hard to help, her.' [*Calendar of Clarendon State Papers*, II, 419]

(The Hague, 20 May 1655) '. . . your wife is resolving whither shee will writ or no therefore I am to say nothing to you from her but will keepe open my letter as long as the post will permitte to expect what good nature will worke which I find now dos not at all for 'tis now eleven of the clock & noe letter comes.' [*Thurloe State Papers*, I, 665]

(Hounslerdike, 21 June 1655) '. . . . your wife desires mee to present her humble duty to you, which is all shee can say, I tell her 'tis because shee thinks of another husband and dos not follow your example, of being as constant a wife as you are a husband, 'tis a frailty they say as given to the sex therefore you will pardon her I hope.' [*Thurloe State Papers*, I, 665]

Some writers (e.g. Hallam, *Constitutional History*, II, 302 n.) have taken it for granted that the 'wife' (though not a legal wife) was Lucy; but a better authority, Sir Arthur Bryant, says she was Jane Lane, who had helped Charles escape after Worcester and was one of Mary's attendants. [*King Charles II*, July 1949 edition, p. 47 n.] The volume in Lambeth Palace Library which holds the originals of the Thurloe letters contains also a list of the code names Charles II used at this time. His own is 'le constant'. Unfortunately the code name against 'M. berlo' has been torn away.

Lucy's Pension Warrant: 'Charls R. Wee do by these presents of Our especial Grace, give and grant unto Mrs Lucy Barlow, an Annuity or yearly Pension of Five thousand Livres, to be paid to her or her Assignes in the City of Antwerp, or in such other convenient place, as she shall desire, at four several payments by equal portions, the first payment to begin from the first of July 1654, and so to continue from three months to three months during her life; with assurance to better the same, when it shall please God to restore us to our Kingdoms.

Given under our Sign Manuel, at our Court at Cologn, this 21 day of January 1655. And in the sixth year of our Reign.

By His Majesties Command.   Edward Nicholas.'

[*Mercurius Politicus*, 10-17 July 1656.]

Daniel O'Neile's Letters. Daniel O'Neile—the most valiant, versatile, adventurous, talkative and amusing of the Cavaliers— served the Stuarts for thirty years as soldier, courtier, spy, negotiator and Gentleman of the Bedchamber; and when he died in 1664 Charles II wrote that ' he was as honest a man as ever lived '. [*Letters*, p. 168] His contemporaries did not all agree with that. Lucy's reputation largely depends on whether the two letters he wrote to Charles from The Hague in February 1656 were the honest reports of a conscientious agent or the malicious lies of a subtle, scheming rogue trying to ruin an honest woman whose continuance in the King's favour blocked his path to riches and power in Whitehall.

(8 February) ' I have hetherto forborne giving your majestie any account of your commands concerning Mrs Barloe, because those that I imployed to hir, brought mee assurances from hir, she would obey your majestie's commands. Of late I am tould she intends nothing less, and that she is assured from Collen your majestie would not have hir son from hir. I am much troubled to see the prejudice hir being here does your majestie; for every idle action of hers brings your Majestie uppon the stage; I am noe less ashamed to have soe much importuned your majestie to have beleeved hir worthy of your care. . . .' [Presumably in escorting her to Liége.]

(14 February) ' Before I took the liberty to writ anything to your majestie of Mrs Barloe, I did sufficiently informe myself of the truth of what I writ, since I had the opportunity to save her from publick scandall at least. Hir mayd, whom she would have killed by thrusting a bodkin into hir eare ass she was asleep, would have accused hir of that, of miscarrying of two children by phissick, and of the infamous manner of hir living with Mr Howard; but I have prevented the mischiefs, partly with threats, butt more with 100 gilders I am to give hir mayd. Hir last mis-

carriage was since Mrs Howard went [to Paris with the Princess Royal], ass the midwyf says to one, that I imploy to hir. Doctor Rufus has given hir phissick, but it was allwayes after hir miscarrying; and though hee knew any thing, it would bee indiscreet to tell it. Therefore I would not attempt him, and the rather, that I was sufficiently assured by those, that were neerer. Though I have saved hir for this tyme, it's not lykly she'le escap when I am gon; for onely the consideratione of your majestie has held Monsieur Heenuleit [Tom Howard's father-in-law; Lady Stanhope's husband] and Monsieur Nertwick, not to have hir banished this toune and country for an infamous person, and by sound of drum. Therefore it were well if your majesty will owen that chyld, to send hir your positive command to deliver him unto whom your Majestie will appoint. I know it from one, who has read my Lord Taaf's letter to hir of the 11th by this last post, that hee tells hir, your majestie has noething more in consideratione than hir sufferings; and that the next monny you can gett or borrow, shall be sent to supply hir. Whyle your majestie incourages any to speak this language, she'le never obey what you will have. The onely way is to necessitat hir, if your majestie can think hir worth your care.' [*Thurloe State Papers*, I, 683-4]

This circumstantial second-hand evidence may be more convincing to many readers than the (perhaps deliberate) contrary memory of Charles Gerard, another of Charles's companions in exile, as recorded in Gilbert Burnet's letter to Lord Halifax of 29 May 1680:

'The King seems to be in good health, but his colour is not good, and he was sullen and avoided the speaking with almost everybody. . . . But that which surpris'd people most, his examining the Earl of Macclesfield upon his knowledge of the Duke of Monmouth's mother being a whore to other people, which that Earl did not remember, though the King gave him a token to call him to mind about it. This is thought an absolute breaking off from all kindness to that Duke.' [*Camden Miscellany*, XI, 30-1]

IX *London: The Tower*   (May-July 1656)

Elizabeth Walter's Will was dated 20 August 1655, and proved
on 8 February 1656; she left all her property to her brother
[-in-law] Peter Gosfright. Administration was granted on 3
March 1657/8 to her sister Margaret, Peter's widow. [Steinman,
p. 94]

Colonel Barkstead's reports on the interrogations of Lucy,
Justus and Thomas Howard on 28 June 1656 are in the *Thurloe
State Papers*, V, 169. Anne Hill, examined twice, spoke at
length. On 26 June she said ' that she hath often heard, that one
of the said children her said lady had by Charles Stuart, and that
the said lady had no other means to maintain her, but what she
hath from the said Charles Stuart, although she lives in a costly
and high manner . . . the said lady told her this informant, she
was, a little before her coming over, with the King, meaning
Charles Stuart; and this informant having conference with the
said lady's brother about it, he swore the said lady had been lately
with the King . . . a night and a day together.' On 2 July Anne
added to what she had already said that she ' never heard, that
the said lady had any husband in Holland, or any other place,
but that those children she had were begotten by Charles Stuart '.
She said that Thomas Howard ' did much frequent' Lucy's
company at The Hague, and that she had overheard Lucy and
Justus discussing a pearl necklace ' which the said lady intimated
to him she had bought; and that they discoursed it must cost
about 1500£.' *Thurloe State Papers,* V, 160-1, 178]

On 1 July Cromwell approved in the Council of State that
' Lucy Barlow, prisoner in the Tower, be sent back to Flanders,
with her child, and Sir John Barkstead to see it done.' [*Calendar
of State Papers, Domestic,* 1656-7, p. 4] The Commonwealth
newspaper, *Mercurius Politicus* for 10-17 July 1656, reporting
this, said that Lucy Barlow ' passeth under the Character of
Charls Stuart's Wife or Mistres, and hath a young Son, whom
she openly declareth to be his; and it generally beleeved, the

Boy being very like him, and both the Mother and Child provided for by him. . . .' After quoting the Pension Warrant found
on her, the journalist continues: 'By this those that hanker after
him may see they are furnished already with an Heir Apparent,
and how well he disposeth of the Collections and Contributions
which they make for him here, towards the maintenance of his
Concubines and Royal Issue. Order is taken forthwith to send
away his Lady of Pleasure, and the young Heir, and set them
on shoar in Flanders, which is no ordinary curtesie.'

Was Lucy a Royalist messenger? Contemporary and modern
accounts of the Royalists in England during the Commonwealth
do not mention her, but that does not prove she was not used
to carry messages, or as a decoy to divert attention from the real
plotters. The account of her contacts with London Royalists in
the 'Letter to a Person of Honour concerning the Black Box'
is hardly reliable.

Monmouth was executed on Tower Hill on 15 July 1685,
denied the day's respite he had pleaded for in the superstitious
hope that, if he could survive the anniversary of his release in
1656, he would be reprieved. Between those years he served as
Captain of the King's Guard and as Commander-in-Chief of the
King's forces.

X *Brussels: The Abandoned Woman*

(July 1656-December 1657)

Lucy's Troubles in Brussels in August 1657. On 1 August
Hyde wrote from Bruges to Ormond: '. . . Here is much talk
here of a certain lady who is at Brussels, and I assure you very
shrewd discourses of it, which will quickly get into England;
I pray let her go to some other place. . . . [*Clarendon State Papers*,
III, 355] Ormond to Hyde, 3 August: 'The lady has now her
sonne and heyre with her, to make up the cry.' [*Calendar of
Clarendon State Papers*, III, 343]

One of Thurloe's spies reported from Brussels on 25 August:
'Tom Howard going yesterday from the king's court, accom-

panied with a Fleming . . . was wounded in the street by a little young gentleman, cousin of Mrs Barlow, who by former challenge demanded satisfaction from Tom. for words dishonouring his cousin. Tom. refusing the demand, the little gentleman found him in his way, and with a stiletto-poiniard struck at his body, and by the other's defence with his right hand, met the point, which entred in by the elbow, and passed out at the hand-wrist; whereat his friend escaped away, and the person, that gave the wound, left him so, thinking he was slain. . . ! ' [*Thurloe State Papers*, VI, 463]

Hyde to Nicholas, Brussels, 27 August: 'We had an odd accident on Friday: . . . a young fellow, kinsman or servant to your client Mrs Barlow, came behind [Howard] and stabbed him with a dagger; by good chance he was then moving his arm to gather up his cloak, and so took the blow through his arm and saved his body, yet with a very dangerous wound, all the arteries being cut; the fellow got into a church and is escaped, but I believe that justice will be very severely prosecuted against both mistress and man. . . .' [*Clarendon State Papers*, III, 357-8]

The Earl of Bristol to Hyde, 2 September: 'You may bee merry concerninge Mrs Barlo, but I assure you I can not bee it, enough to answere your levityes.' [*Calendar of Clarendon State Papers*, III, 354] Neither the end of the affair, nor Hyde's merriment are recorded.

Lucy's Troubles at Brussels in December 1657 form the subject of three long letters, 6, 10 and 13 December [*Clarendon State Papers*, III, 382-3], between M. Egidio Mottet, Secretary to Don Alonzo de Cardenas, the Governor's Intendant, and the Marquis of Ormond, who was with the King at Bruges. Don Alonzo himself wrote to the King on the 6th about the ' attempt made last night by Col. Slingsby to carry Mrs Barlow to one of the public prisons of the city, and to separate her from her son, which she resisted with great outcries, embracing her son; the whole street was gathered together, scandalized at the Colonel's violence, who consented at length that the lady and her son should stay at the Earl of Castlehaven's house for that night.' Don

Alonzo said that 'having been informed of the occurence (which everybody condemns)' he 'has replaced Mrs Barlow with her son in her house, on her giving security to await the knowledge of the King's will. . . .' [*Calendar of Clarendon State Papers*, III, 392-3]

In apologising for 'the proceeding of Monsieur Slingsby' Mottet said that the people of Brussels 'found this action most barbarous, abominable and most unnatural; and the worst of all is, that Sir Arthur doth report and say to all, that the King hath given him order for it.' Ormond replied that the King 'takes your proceeding in the business of Mrs Barlow very kindly . . . he is pleased to acknowledge that he gave order to Sir Arthur Slingsby in a quiet and silent way, if it could be, to get the child out of the mother's hands, with purposes of advantage to them both, but he never understood it should be attempted with that noise and scandal that hath happened. . . . His Majesty persists in his desire to have the child delivered into such hands as he shall appoint, and will take himself to be much obliged to you if by your means it may be effected. . . . It will also be a great charity to the child, and in the conclusion to the mother, if she shall now at length retire herself to such a way of living as may redeem in some measure the reproach her past ways have brought upon her. If she consents not to this, she will add to all her former follies a most unnatural one in reference to her child, who by her obstinacy will be exposed to all the misery and reproach that must attend her, when neither of them is any further cared for or owned by his Majesty; but that on the contrary he will take any good office done to her as an injury to him, and as a supporting of her in her mad disobedience to his pleasure. . . .'

M. Mottet assured Ormond that 'Since the very first day that Mrs Barlow came to my quarter I did procure to make her understand and persuade her, that it was her convenience to oblige the King in delivering the child into his hands, and her ruin in not doing it; but all that I could have of her hitherto is, that she declareth to be content to leave the child to be bred and instructed as the King shall appoint, so that she may live at

Brussels in the house of that person whom the King shall choose
with her consent (Slingsby excepted) to have the care and keeping of the child, in which case she desireth that a pension be
settled for his subsistence, and a supply for her present necessity. . . .'

(Would the people of Brussels have been shocked at Slingsby's
conduct if Lucy had been a notorious prostitute?)

Slingsby justified himself in a long letter to the King dated
22 December, saying that Don Alonzo was 'most infinitely out
of countenance' when he pointed out that he had cause for a
civil action against Mrs Barlow, which 'her ill behaviour to your
Majesty gained me a liberty of prosecuting her by the Justice
for my due', and when he threatened to proceed against M.
Mottet and Lord Castlehaven 'till such time as they either pay
me my money, or render the prisoner into the hands of the
Justice'. He went on to say that Daniel O'Neile had told him
'that it would be an acceptable service to your Majesty to get
certain papers and letters out of her hands that concern your
Majesty' and he suggested that the Spaniards should be asked
to search her trunks in his presence. [Clarendon State Papers,
III, 384-5]

XI *Flanders: Battle*   (January 1658)

Disney's vague evidence in the Black Box enquiry associated
Prodgers with the kidnapping of Lucy's son. [Calendar of State
Papers, Domestic, 1679-80, pp. 447-8] The Heroick Life of Monmouth opens with a long, but hardly credible, account of an
earlier abduction, apparently based on his recollection of an
incident when a baby.

XII *Calais: Final Surrender*   (January 1658)

There is no historical basis for Charles's visit to Calais. On
12/22 January 1658, Don Alonzo wrote to Hyde that 'Madame
Werlo desires to place the child at the absolute disposal of his
Majesty'. [Calendar of Clarendon State Papers, IV, 4-5]

On 25 March/4 April 1658, Thomas Ross, who later served Monmouth as tutor and secretary for many years, wrote from Brussels to Nicholas: 'The King sent me to take his little son out of the hands he was in, and bestow him for awhile in a place out of the knowledge of his mother or anyone else, but such as I took to help me, himself, and your younger brother. I wondered at the King's choosing me for this task. I believe I am designed for his tutor. He cannot be safe from his mother's intrigues where he is. It is a pity so pretty a child should be in hands that have neglected to teach him to read, or to tell 20 though he has much wit and great desire to learn.' [Calendar of State Papers, Domestic, 1657-8, p. 342]

Postscript

The last glimpse of Lucy alive is in a report from a Thurloe spy from Bruges on 26 August 1658 that Lord Taafe had killed a man in a duel, and that 'There was another combat betweene Madam Barlow, who bor Charles Stuart two children, and doctor Floid. He got the wors, and is gon for Holland. Hee was one of C. Stuart his chapplins. . . .' [Thurloe State Papers, VII, 337] I think Steinman (p. 106) was mistaken in identifying this obscure Dr Floid as the famous William Lloyd, Bishop of St Asaph, etc.

We don't know what Lucy died of; there is no need to believe James II's sneer that she died of 'the disease incident to her profession'. Steinman [Addenda, pp. 7-8] suggests that she was buried in 'the Huguenot cemetery in the Fauxbourg St Germain, Paris', which has long since been built over. Bishop White Kennet wrote that William Erskine 'the Master of the Charterhouse, a Scots Gentleman, long in the Service of King Charles abroad, had the particular Care and Custody of the Duke of Monmouth's Mother and buried her at Paris. He was often Express in this Matter, and said positively, the King had never any Intention to Marry her; and that indeed she did not deserve

any such good Intention towards her, being a very ill woman.'
[*Complete History*, 1719, III, 366, n.]

Lucy's Estate. Steinman printed [Addenda, p. 7] 'a literal
copy' of 'the Administration entry in the register of the Prerogative Court': 'December, 1658. Lucy Walter al's Barlow. On
the sixt Day issued forth Letters of Ad'con to Anne Busfeild
wife of John Busfeild ye Aunt and next of Kinne of Lucy Walter
al's Barlow late in ye parts beyond ye seas, Spinster, Dec'd. To
adter ye goods, ch'ells and debts of ye said Dec'd. Shee being
first sworne truely to Administer &c.'

We have no indication of the nature or value of the estate;
but Lucy may well have had an interest in family property in
England or Wales.

Selective Bibliography

The eight successive attempts at a biography of Lucy Walter have been by: John Heneage Jesse in *Memoirs of the Court of England during the Reign of the Stuarts*, 1840, III, 362-9; The Rev. George Roberts in *Life of Monmouth*, 1844, I, 1-7; G. Steinman Steinman in *Althorp Memoirs*, 1869, pp. 77-116 and Addenda, 1880; Thomas Seccombe in the *Dictionary of National Biography*, article on Lucy Walter, 1899; G. D. Gilbert 'Some Evidence for a Brief for the Defence', Appendix to Routledge's *Memoirs of the Court of England in 1675*, 1913; G. Allan Heron *Lucy Walter*, 1929; Lord George Scott *Lucy Walter: Wife or Mistress*, 1947; Sir J. F. Rees in the *Dictionary of Welsh Biography*, article on Lucy Walter.

See also chapters by: Christopher Cobbe-Webbe in *Haverfordwest and its Story*, 1882, pp. 43-4; Edward Laws in *History of Little England Beyond Wales*, 1888, pp. 352-8; Allan Fea in *Some Beauties of the Seventeenth Century*, 1906, pp. 128-46; Francis Green, 'Walter of Roch Castle' in *West Wales Historical Records*, 1915, V, 271-86; Sir J. F. Rees in *Studies in Welsh History*, 1947, Chapter VIII, 'The Parents of Lucy Walter'; Plantagenet Somerset Fry in *Mysteries of History*, 1957, pp. 113-25, 'Was Monmouth Legitimate?'; and A. L. Morton, 'Small Finds' in *The Amateur Historian*, Autumn, 1962.

For fictional portraits of Lucy see *The Perplex'd Prince* (Anon., 1682); *The Prince Passes* (F. J. E. Bennett, c. 1935); *Young*

Jemmy (Elizabeth D'Oyley, 1947); *The Wandering Prince* (Jean Plaidy, 1956).

The basic contemporary materials for a biography of Lucy Walter are in the *Calendars of State Papers (Domestic)* and *(Venetian)*, *of Treasury Books and Papers, of the Committees for the Advance of Money and for Compoundings*, and *of the Clarendon State Papers*; in the *Clarendon* and *Thurloe State Papers*; in Clarendon's *History of the Rebellion* and the *Continuation*; in the *House of Lords' Records* and the *Reports of the Historical Manuscripts Commission*; Carte's *Life of Ormond* and *Ormond Papers*; Collins' *Sydney Family Papers*; Dalrymple's *Memoirs of Great Britain and Ireland*; Lewys Dwnn's *Heraldic Visitations of Wales*; Ellis's *Original Letters*; John Evelyn's *Diary* (Bray's 4-volume edition and de Beer's 6-volume edition); Robert Ferguson's *Letters to a Person of Honour* and *Heroick Life* of the Duke of Monmouth; J. T. Gilbert's two histories of the Irish Wars, 1641-52; the *Memoirs of James II* (Macpherson, 1775; Stanier Clarke, 1816; A. Lytton Sells, 1962); *Miscellanea Aulica*, 1702; *Nicholas Papers*; Pepys' *Diary*; *State Trials* (Algernon Sidney, William Disney); Warburton's *Memorials of Prince Rupert and the Cavaliers*; Anthony A Wood's *Fasti*; *Poems and Affairs of State* and other collections of seventeenth-century poems and pamphlets.

See also the *Letters* of Bishop Burnet (Camden Misc.); Charles II (edited by Sir Arthur Bryant); Henry Savile to Rochester; Henry Sydney; and Lord Hatton; the *Memoirs* of the Earl of Ailesbury; the Duke of Berwick; John Sheffield, Duke of Bucks; Gramont; the Duchesse de Montpensier; Sir John Reresby; and Princess Sophia; and the contemporary histories by Burnet, Echard, White Kennet, Roger North, Oldmixon, Sandford & Stebbing, and Welwood; also Harris (1766).

I have also consulted all the standard nineteenth-century historians who deal with the period, and, among other moderns, Maurice Ashley, Sir Arthur Bryant, Sir George Clark, Godfrey Davies, Paul H. Hardacre, I. Deane Jones, J. R. Jones, David Ogg, David Underdown and C. V. Wedgwood; also many biographies of Charles II, the Duke of Monmouth and their contemporaries and books about their times, notably those by S. Elliott Hoskins, C. J. Lyon, Eva Scott, Allan Fea, Osmund Airy, A. I. Dasent, Elizabeth D'Oyley, Jane Lane, Hester W. Chapman and Iris Morley; and articles in *History Today*.

Finally, I must express my gratitude to the Librarians of the British Museum, the House of Lords, Lambeth Palace and the Westminster City Libraries for allowing me the facilities for research, and to their staffs for their advice, assistance and courtesy.

Frank Arthur